Gems TV Guide to Gems and Jewellery 2006

By Gems TV

Welcome to Gems TV

Our dedicated team of over 1,000 crattsmen and jewellers design and create an exclusive range of stunning jewellery.

Whether you are a collector of gemstones or a lover of colourful jewellery, you can now cut out the middlemen by buying direct from one of the world's largest gemstone suppliers.

Gems TV specialises in sourcing only the most beautiful gemstones from the four corners of the globe and setting them in gorgeous handcrafted jewellery, making these stunning creations available direct to you.

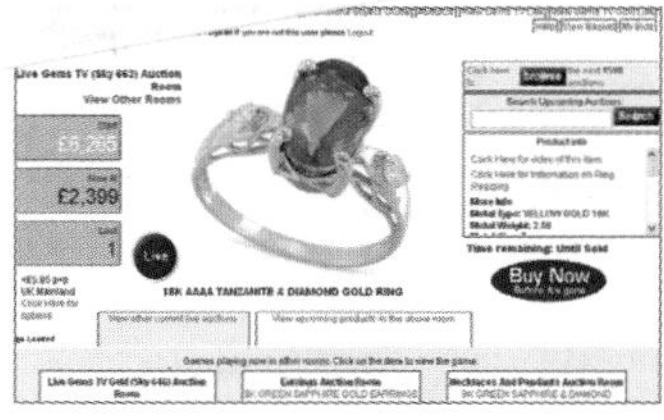

In Europe visit our website: www.GemsTV.com

In America and Asia visit our website: www.Thaigem.com

Debby Cavill
Gems TV's Chief of Global Jewellery Design

GUIDE TO GEMS & JEWELLERY

This book has been written to provide information on gems and jewellery to hobbyists, collectors and, of course, to those who wear jewellery. Neither the publisher nor the authors will be held liable or responsible to any person or entity with respect to loss or damage as a result of the information supplied in this book, whether caused or said to be caused by a direct or indirect result of its contents.

For further information and the latest updates on the colourful world of gemstones, please visit www.GemsTV.com

Please direct enquiries to either:

Gems TV (UK)
PO Box 12916
Redditch
B97 9BT

Gems TV (Thailand)
Thaigem Building
23/999 Yannaviroch Road
Chanthaburi, Thailand 22000

Published by Gems TV (UK) Ltd
Printed in the UK

First Printed 2005

ISBN-13: 978-0-9551491-0-8
ISBN-10: 0-9551491-0-X

CONTENTS

FOREWORD

Since antiquity, kings and queens and the rich and famous have all worn coloured gemstone jewellery. Their rarity and beauty is such that throughout the ages, they have been believed to hold mystical and spiritual powers. History books are full of stories and adventures that feature gems and even the Bible makes numerous references to them.

During the 20th Century, as a result of clever marketing campaigns, Diamonds have become the most renowned gemstone. While nobody doubts the attraction of their brilliance (even though several other coloured gems have a higher refractive index) or their durability (Diamonds are the hardest of all gemstones), in the folklore and legends of centuries gone by, it is the coloured gemstone and not the Diamond that has dominated. Presenting over 490 gem types sourced from over 60 countries, Gems TV is proud to continue this tradition. In this guide, and of course live on Gems TV, you'll discover a dazzling array of coloured gemstones well suited to every pocket and every taste.

Throughout history, many legends have arisen regarding the esoteric and metaphysical properties of gemstones and even today, belief in their powers continues to be widespread. In the A to Z section of this book you will find details on both folklore and gemology. When you read about the beliefs of spiritual healers, please remember that little scientific evidence has been found to substantiate these beliefs. If this area of gem lore interests you, there are numerous books on the subject and a quick search on the Internet will yield thousands of results.

With hundreds of different gem types on offer at Gems TV, 365 days a year, this guide is intended to give you a background into those gems that we feel will form the backbone of our collection throughout 2006. However, the one thing that you can be sure about Mother Nature, is that nothing can be taken for granted. We therefore cannot guarantee the availability of all gems featured in this guide, but likewise I am confident that we will be able to bring you many additional gems that to date we have yet to feature.

"Happy gem hunting!"

Don Kogen, the Gem Hunter

Our A-Z of Gems provides an invaluable insight to the legends, colours and diversity of the wonderful world of gemstones.

A-Z OF GEMS CONTENTS

As several gems are sometimes referred to by different names, if you cannot find what you are looking for in the A to Z section, please use the index on page 192.

AGATE

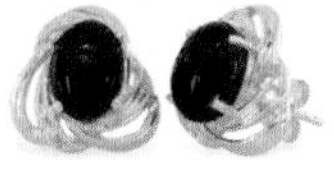

Black Agate set in sterling silver

A beautiful example of Fire Agate set in 9k gold with a traditional cabochon cut

A 3ct Moss Agate with an unusual 6 claw setting

AGATE:	Mentioned in the Bible
Locations:	Australia, Brazil, Canada, Germany, India, Madagascar, Scotland, U.S.A, Mexico, South Africa, Uruguay
Colours Found:	Multiple
Typical Cuts:	Cabochon, ornamentals
Family:	Chalcedony
Hardness:	6.50 - 7.00
Refractive Index:	1.53 - 1.54
Relative Density:	2.55 - 2.64

Agate is a form of Chalcedony and its name was derived from the site of its initial discovery, the River Achates (now Dirillo), in southwest Sicily. You will often find beautifully flowing patterns within the gem, which are caused by the presence of manganese and iron.

Legends and lore

Said by the ancients to render the wearer invisible, Agate has been admired by humanity for thousands of years. Valued by the Ancient Sumerians and Egyptians, Agate is one of the oldest known gems.

It is mentioned in the Bible as being one of the "Stones of Fire" (Ezekiel 28:13-16) and was also given to Moses (Exodus 28:15-30). A variety of Agate, Sardonyx is one of the twelve gemstones set in the foundations of the city walls of Jerusalem (Revelations 21:19).

Agate was especially valued during medieval times where one of the more outlandish uses was to bind an Agate gem to each horn of an oxen to ensure a good harvest.

Agate is believed to cure insomnia, ensure pleasant dreams, protect from danger and promote strength and healing. Wearers are believed to become temperate, content and cautious. In antiquity, Agate was regarded as a cooling gem, capable of reducing fever, quenching thirst, quieting the pulse and ensuring good health and a long and prosperous life.

Just the facts

The main conditions necessary for Agate formation are the presence of silica from devitrified volcanic ash, water from rainfall or ground sources, manganese, iron and other mineral oxides that form the bands and inclusions.

Agate comes in many different forms ranging from transparent to opaque. Varieties include Blue Agate, Blue Lace Agate, Crazy Lace Agate, Green Agate, Indian Agate, Moss Agate, Fire Agate, Tree Agate, Onyx, Sardonyx and Wood Agate.

ALEXANDRITE

Discovered in Russia's Ural Mountains on the birthday of Tsar Alexander in 1830, Alexandrite is one of the world's most valuable gems. Often described as "Emerald by day" and "Ruby by night", when viewed under sunlight, Alexandrite appears teal to forest green but, when seen by candlelight, hues of violet, crimson-red, purple or orange appear.

Scant availability, remarkable colour change, excellent durability and a sparkling "adamantine" or Diamond-like lustre, make Alexandrite a "must have" for any true jewellery connoisseur. A rare variety of Chrysoberyl, Alexandrite ranks alongside Tanzanite and Padparadscha Sapphire as one of the world's most desired coloured gemstones.

8 oval cut Alexandrite gemstones weighing in at 1.75ct

Legends and lore

Alexandrite was named after the young Tsarevitch, who was crowned Tsar Alexander II in 1855. Allegedly, Alexandrite was discovered on his birthday in the year when the Russian heir apparent came of age.

The fortuity of the discovery of Alexandrite on the future Tsar's birthday was considered manifold, as the colours displayed by this unusual gem can mirror the imperial Russian colours of red and green. Possessing dual nationalistic connotations, Alexandrite quickly gained popularity in Russia, where it was believed to bring good luck.

Sophisticated beauty containing 56 Alexandrite gems

Alexandrite's relatively recent discovery has left it little time to gather tales of myth and superstition. Nevertheless, Alexandrite (along with Pearl and Moonstone), is already an official birthstone for June.

An oval cut Alexandrite gemstone weighing in at 2.2ct from Tanzania

Just the facts

In gemology, it is correct to call any Chrysoberyl that changes colour Alexandrite. The nomenclature is not dependent on the colours of the change. In fact, the extent of colour change in most Alexandrite isn't always that obvious to the untrained eye.

An example of Alexandrite from Minas Gerais Brazil

ALEXANDRITE

A stunning pairing of Alexandrite and 9k white gold

The natural lustre of Alexandrite brilliantly accentuated by our expert gem cutters

Traditional and glamourous, Alexandrite's green tones work to stunning effect in this bracelet

15 oval cut Alexandrites prong set into 9k gold

Interestingly, the colour change effect is not unique to Alexandrite. Many gem types display colour change (e.g. Sapphire and Garnet). However, the degree of colour change exhibited by Alexandrite can be the most extreme encountered in natural gems.

Alexandrite's colour change is dependent on pure light sources (i.e. pure candescent light to pure incandescent light), for example sunlight to candlelight.

Arguably, one of the best uses of Alexandrite is in earrings and pendants. In this position, the vibrancy of Alexandrite's colour change is easily noticed. Alexandrite rings are also popular, as it is a very tough gem with a hardness that is only transcended by Rubies, Sapphires and Diamonds.

Alexandrite is normally included. Just like Ruby and Rubellite these inclusions are all part of Mother Nature's fingerprints. As there has been a flood of synthetic Alexandrite onto the market in recent years, many people find the fact that the natural gem is included provides them with comfort that they are buying the real thing.

Where few inclusions are visible to the naked eye, prices rise stratospherically. Unlike its non-colour changing brother Chrysoberyl, Alexandrite has been placed in the Type II category of coloured gems, meaning that inclusions are typical.

Alexandrite is fashioned into a wide variety of shapes and styles. However, in order to maximise the carat weight (due to the high expense of rough Alexandrite), the shapes are often tightly bound to that of the rough gem. However, at Gems TV our focus is always on maximising the beauty of a gem, rather than focusing purely on the carat weight. This is why you will often find on our Authenticity Certificates gem weights such as 0.997ct.

The original source of arguably the finest specimens, Russian Alexandrite possesses an historical pedigree that has long demanded premium prices when compared to Alexandrites from other locales.

ALEXANDRITE *(RUSSIAN)*

Early one chilly October morning in 1830, a Russian peasant was making his way through the silver birch forests along the banks of the Tokovaya River, in the Ural Mountains. Tripping on the roots of a large tree felled by a storm, he discovered some green gemstones. Quickly identified as Emeralds, by 1831 this deposit was being mined.

The Tokovaya Emerald mines also yielded other gemstones, including a new one that had the strange ability to change colour. When viewed under sunlight, rich green colours appeared but, when seen by candlelight, it displayed red hues.

The gem was named "Alexandrite" after Tsar Alexander II and it quickly created a sensation. Everyone wanted an Alexandrite! But this was certainly no fun for the miners. Imagine working through long winters plagued by biting cold and blinding snowdrifts. Summer brought no respite, just great swarms of mosquitoes! Following the narrow Alexandrite veins with hand dug trenches, open pits and small tunnels, mining was primitive to say the least!

While beautiful Alexandrite is available from other locales, the finest Alexandrite still hails from the Tokovaya deposit. Although the Tokovaya deposit closed after only a few decades, occasionally, a second look with more modern techniques yields a few surprises. Regardless, very little Russian Alexandrite is available and prices reflect this. Russian Alexandrite above half a carat is especially rare and almost impossible to find!

Thankfully, Don "the gem hunter" has managed to turn back time. We are delighted to offer an amazing selection of Russian Alexandrite exclusively to Gems TV customers!

Don Kogen, the Gem Hunter says:

"Without doubt, Alexandrite along with Tanzanite are two of the most glorious gems that we set into jewellery. During my 15 years travelling the world sourcing gems, the relationships I have built to source these gems are the very best."

A rare example of Russian Alexandrite set into an elegant pendant

Set into 18k gold, this beauty was unearthed in early 2005 and sold on Gems TV in August the same year

A beautiful trilogy ring,featuring three perfectly matched square gems

Russian Alexandrite can possess both rich green and red hues

ALEXANDRITE *(CAT'S EYE)*

Coveted for their beautiful and mysterious optical effects, when you look at a Cat's Eye Alexandrite you can see a single band of light on its surface.

Technically known as the "Asteric Effect", this intriguing phenomenon is unique to the world of gemstones. It is caused by minerals reflecting a band of light back to the eye like a mirror.

Cat's Eye Alexandrite makes particularly stunning signet rings and is a powerful display of a unique sense of style.

9.4ct of Cat's Eye Alexandrite went into making this unique and elegant bracelet

6 perfectly colour matched Cat's Eye Alexandrite gems

A distinctive design perfectly complemented by the use of Cat's Eye Alexandrite

Gems TV's Chief of Global Jewellery Design, Debby Cavill's father has over 30 years experience in the manufacturing jewellery trade in the UK.

He had heard of Alexandrite and knew of the rarity but had never actually seen one until seeing it through Gems TV!

He said: *"I would be surprised if more than a handful of retailers in the UK could even supply Alexandrite and the majority of retailers in the UK would never even know of the existence of this beautiful gemstone!"*

Steve Bennett, Gems TV MD says:

"I wear my Alexandrite Cat's Eye ring nearly every day. There is something magical and mystical about it. At times, the optical illusion of the chatoyancy within the gem will even appear as if it is winking at you - simply fascinating!

With so much history surrounding Alexandrite, I often launch into a massive story about the gemstone when asked about my ring. And because of its rarity and deep green colour, when alone and quietly sitting and admiring it, the feeling I experience is one of calmness.

In fact, the reason why the relaxation room for actors and presenters at all TV companies is painted green and referred to as 'The Green Room', is because the colour is said to have a calming and relaxing effect."

ALEXANDRITE:	June's birthstone
Locations:	Brazil, Russia, Tanzania, Brazil, Mozambique, Madagascar, Sri Lanka
Colours Found:	Green, yellowish green, brownish green
Typical Cuts:	Brilliant, marquise, heart, oval
Family:	Chrysoberyl
Hardness:	8.50
Refractive Index:	1.74 - 1.75
Relative Density:	3.71

AMBER

Amber is the ancient and fossilised resin of long dead trees that grew in forests millions and millions of years ago.

Over the eons, chemical and physical changes occurred, fossilising the resin to produce the Amber we know today.

Research indicates that Amber ranges from about 2 million to 360 million years in age, although most gem-quality Amber ranges from 5 million to 50 million years.

Amber is a unique gem. On top of its beauty, Amber bequeaths much valuable scientific data through its ability to act as a window on the past. Its unique ability to preserve the organic tissues of prehistoric life forms is highly valued by both gem collectors and scientists alike.

Legends and lore

In classical times, Amber was used medicinally and was also believed to offer a magical light for the deceased as they progressed through the underworld.

Powers attributed to Amber include love, humour, joy, strength, luck, healing, protection, and the ability to calm hyperactivity and stressed nerves.

Just the facts

When you rub Amber, static electricity is generated. In fact, the word electricity is derived from the ancient Greek word for Amber, "Elektron" or "Sun Made".

The organic inclusions commonly found in Amber include plant debris, small animals and a variety of pre-historic insects. These ancient creatures are predominantly extinct ancestors of today's cockroaches, ants, termites, caddis flies, centipedes, crickets, scorpions and millipedes.

Some larger organisms, such as snakes, have also been recorded. These preserved life forms were trapped by fresh sticky resin that oozed from coniferous trees millions of years ago.

A simple and eyecatching design containing this amazing prehistoric gem

9 pieces of stunning Lithuanian Amber

A regal design with radiant Amber results in this majestic necklace

AMBER

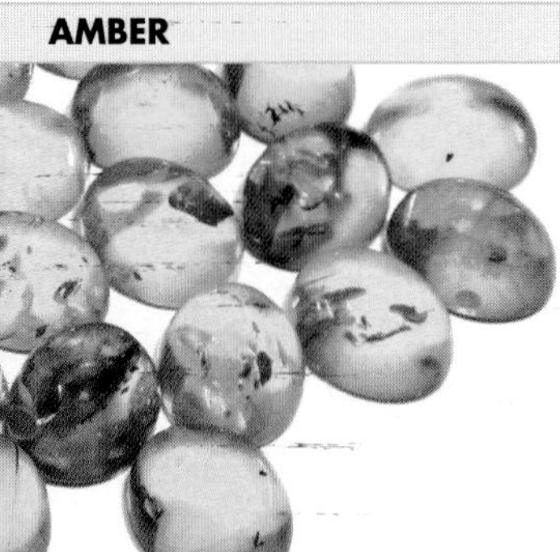

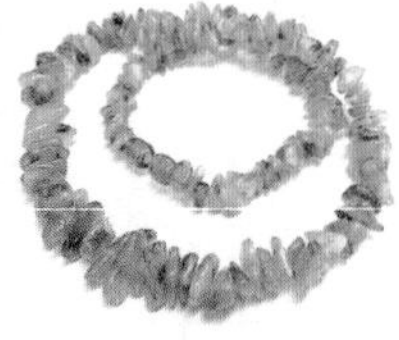

This contemporary necklace contains 16 inches of beautiful Amber

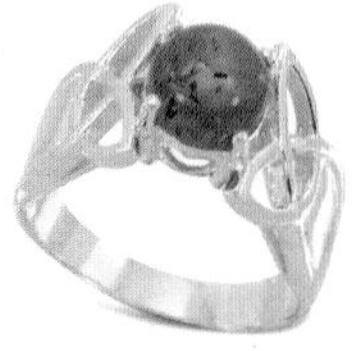

A simple and eyecatching design containing this amazing pre-historic gem

Contemporary style and ancient beauty

AMBER:	Preserves pre-historic life forms
Locations:	Germany, England, Scotland, Romania, Russia, Dominican Republic, Mexico
Colours Found:	Golden yellow, pale yellow, deep cherry-red to dark brown
Typical Cuts:	Cabochons, beads, ornamentals
Family:	Organics
Hardness:	2.00 - 3.00
Refractive Index:	1.54
Relative Density:	1.05 - 1.10

Entombed and preserved in the Amber, the insects are visible in almost perfect condition, showing the position they were in when they were entombed millions of years ago.

The most valued variety of Amber for manufacturing jewellery and decorative objects is Baltic Amber. Occurring in yellow, golden and brown colours, Baltic Amber is also known as Succinite after its parent tree Pinus Succinfera, that was common in the Tertiary period, some 50 million years ago. At present, the primary source of Baltic Amber is found in the various deposits around the Russian port of Kaliningrad and the old German enclave of Koenigsberg. Incredibly light, Amber is occasionally buoyant in salt water and is sometimes transported long distances by the sea, having been found as far away as the beaches of England and Scotland. It is from this ability that it gains one of its common names, "Seastone".

Since the Jurassic Park movies, interest in insect and animal included Amber has exploded, making it highly collectable. In regards to the film Jurassic Park, the alleged source of the dinosaur DNA was Dominican Amber. However, Dominican Amber is thought to be about 25 million years too young to truly contain Dinosaur DNA, making the plot slightly inaccurate.

However, other Amber sources from around the world could potentially contain the genetic material of these avian ancestors.

In 1994, a molecular biologist from California reported that he had extracted DNA from an insect sealed in Amber 120 to 130 million years ago. Dr. Raul Canu claimed the insect was trapped when dinosaurs ruled the Earth; leading people to speculate that Michael Crichton's novel could one day become a scientific reality.

Although a fossilised plant resin that generally consists of organic carbon, hydrogen and oxygen structures, the composition varies depending on the type of parental plant species.

AMETHYST

Dionysus, known for his love of grape juice, was the Greek god of wine. However, after a few goblets he became a little confrontational. One day in the forest, with goblet in hand, the tipsy Dionysus took insult from a passing mortal who refused to show him respect. The incident provoked his wrath and Dionysus swore revenge on the next mortal whom he saw.

Along came Amethyst, a beautiful young maiden on her way to pay tribute to the goddess, Diana. Dionysus targeted Amethyst as the object of his revenge, and, with the snap of his fingers, he summoned two ferocious tigers to devour the girl. As Dionysus sat back to enjoy the spectacle, Amethyst cried out to her goddess, Diana. Seeing what was about to happen Diana transformed Amethyst into a glimmering pure White Quartz statue, protecting her from the ferocious tigers. Moved with guilt, Dionysus realised the ruthlessness of his actions and began to weep with sorrow. As the tears dripped into his goblet, Dionysus collapsed, spilling the tear-tainted wine onto the statue of Amethyst. The White Quartz absorbed the wine's colour creating the coloured gem that we refer to today as Amethyst, the gemstone of the gods.

A simple yet elegant pair of Madagascan Amethyst earrings, featuring a modern prong setting

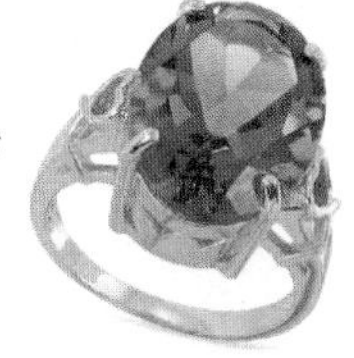

An impressive 7.7ct Amethyst ring, displaying precise faceting

Legends and lore

With the mythology surrounding the origin of Amethyst, it is perhaps fitting that, according to spiritual healers, it is considered a talisman to prevent drunkenness. Indeed, it derives its name from the Greek word "Amethystos", meaning "Not Drunk". It is believed that Amethyst holds the power to change anger into tranquillity. It is also believed that Amethyst is a protective gem that bounces off psychic attack, reverting negative energy into positive. As a gemstone of great healing and meditative powers, Amethyst is a purifier of energies of the mind, body and spirit.

17 oval Amethysts beautifully combined with Nigerian Pink Tourmaline

A natural blend of Amethyst and Green Sapphire to create a sophisticated pendant

The chief mining areas for Brazilian Amethyst are Minas Gerais, Bahia and Maraba. Brazilian Amethyst varies in colour saturation from pale to medium lilac. Neighbouring Uruguay offers spectacularly beautiful varieties of Amethyst and new deposits have been found there recently.

AMETHYST

The flawless faceting on this gem brings out the brilliance of colour inside

The lilac hues of this gem are beautifully enhanced by the pairing of Pink Tourmaline and 9k white gold

AMETHYST:	February's birthstone
Locations:	Madagascar, Zambia, Kenya, Brazil, Uruguay
Colours Found:	Shades of purple with red and blue flashes
Typical Cuts:	Round brilliant, fancy shapes
Family:	Quartz
Hardness:	7.00
Refractive Index:	1.54 - 1.55
Relative Density:	6.50

Amethyst is thought to encourage celibacy and symbolise piety. It was a key feature in the decoration of Catholic churches in the Middle Ages. Amethyst was considered to be the "Papal Stone" and even today bishops still wear Amethyst rings.

Just The Facts

Amethyst is a variety of Quartz that occurs in a transparent light lavender/lilac to deep purple. It is these deeper, more intense colours that are considered the most precious. Amethyst's shades of purple have served as a symbol of royalty throughout history. Kings and queens, as well as leading lights in religious sects, have long treasured it because of its rich, royal colour.

The history of adornment can be traced back to the Minoan period in Greece (circa 2500 BC), where Amethyst has been found as polished cabochons set into gold rings. Popular in the classic parure of the 19th Century, Amethyst was a favourite gem featured in Art Nouveau jewellery.

Like many other gemstones, the quality of Amethyst varies according to its source. Amethyst from the Americas can be found in large sizes as opposed to African Amethyst (typically mined in Madagascar), which is small but carries a higher saturation in colour. The Siberian variety is deep purple with occasional red and blue flashes and commands the highest price. However, the most prolific origin is Brazil, and, if we were to believe that Dionysus' wine was indeed the source of its colour, Brazilian Amethyst would have been born from the finest vintages.

What our Craftsmen say:

Miss Natthika Sangsot - Jeweller

"Gems TV offers one of the world's most extensive collections of Amethyst gemstones, including the world's best deep purple Amethyst with red flashes from Uruguay. This stunning gem is ideal for all kinds of jewellery including earrings, necklaces and rings."

AMETRINE

Ametrine is one of the world's most unusual gemstones in that it is actually two gems in one! Ametrine blends the golden sunburst of Citrine with the purple sunset of Amethyst.

Legends and lore

Ametrine is said to possess all the metaphysical benefits of both Amethyst and Citrine, as well as its own unique properties. Ametrine is said to aid meditation, relieve tension, disperse negativity and help eliminate prejudice.

Just the facts

The unusual colour variation found in Ametrine is due to the presence of iron in different oxidation states within the crystalline structure. Exactly how this comes about is not fully understood.

4 baguette cut Ametrines displayed in a beautifully unusual bar setting

The world's only source of Ametrine, the Bolivian Anahi mine became famous in the 17th Century when a Spanish Conquistador received it as a dowry after marrying an Ayoreos princess named Anahi.

A Brazilian Ametrine pendant showing the amazing split colour quality of this rare and unusual gemstone

Ametrine has only been readily available to the consumer market since 1980 when material from the Anahi mine in Bolivia began to appear on the market in larger quantities. Before 1980, it was considered to be quite unusual and was known as Amethyst-Citrine Quartz, Trystine or Golden Amethyst.

The colour split is usually highlighted by cutting the gem into long shapes ideal for Ametrine earrings and Ametrine necklaces. Larger Ametrine gemstones make particularly enchanting pendants, perfect for evening wear.

A fine split in the colours and the intensity of colour are the most important aspects to consider when evaluating Ametrine.

This is an amazing gemstone with a split personality. When we receive it in the Design Centre we always try and ensure that both the Amethyst and the Citrine are clearly visible to the naked eye.

AMETRINE:	Colour split
Locations:	Bolivia
Colours Found:	Purple, golden
Typical Cuts:	Octagon, emerald
Family:	Quartz
Hardness:	7.00
Refractive Index:	1.54 - 1.55
Relative Density:	6.50

AMMONITE

AMMONITE:	415 Million years old
Locations:	U.S.A, Canada
Colours Found:	Multiple
Typical Cuts:	Cabochon
Family:	Organics
Hardness:	5.00 - 6.00
Refractive Index:	1.52 - 1.67
Relative Density:	2.80

Rarer than Diamond, Ammonite is the fossilised remains of a squid-like creature from over 65 million years ago!

Ammonite is named after "Ammon", the ancient Egyptian god of life and reproduction, because the shell of the Ammonite is similar in appearance to the ram-headed deity's horns.

For a similar reason (along with a legend of prosperity), the Blackfoot Tribe of North America knows Ammonite as the "Buffalo Stone".

Legends and lore

The Navajo people carried Ammonite in their medicine bags for health and good hunting.

The Roman historian, Pliny the Elder, regarded Ammonite as the holiest gemstone because it was said to evoke prophetic dreams.

This gem did not make an appearance at Gems TV in 2005. However, our gem hunters are more optimistic for the future.

ANDALUSITE

Mined primarily in Brazil and Sri Lanka, Andalusite also occurs in Spain, Austria, California, U.S.A. and China

ANDALUSITE:	Pleochroism, trichroic
Locations:	Mozambique, Kenya, Sri Lanka, Brazil, Spain, Austria, U.S.A, China
Colours Found:	White, red, brown, orange, green
Typical Cuts:	Rectangular cushion, round brilliant
Family:	Andalusite
Hardness:	4.50 - 7.00
Refractive Index:	1.71 - 1.73
Relative Density:	3.56 - 3.68

Andalusite gets its name from the site of its discovery, the Spanish Province of Andalusia.

Legends and lore

Andalusite is considered by crystal healers to be a gemstone that enhances intellect, problem solving abilities and mental clarity.

It is also mentioned as being conducive to the receipt of messages from the netherworld.

Just the facts

When cutting most pleochroic gemstones (Tanzanite, Iolite, etc), cutters typically try to minimise the pleochroism and maximise the single most prominent colour.

Interestingly, Andalusite is the opposite, as cutters try to orient the gem to get a pleasing mix of orangey brown, yellowish green and gold colours.

When cut successfully, Andalusite looks unlike any other gemstone, displaying patterns of colour dancing around its facets.

APATITE

While it sounds as though it is hungry, it's actually trying to fool you! The name Apatite comes from the Greek word "Apatao", meaning "To Deceive", as Apatite has often been confused with gems such as Paraiba Tourmaline, Peridot (Olivine) and Beryl.

Ironically, the phosphates in bones and teeth of all vertebrate animals are members of the Apatite group, so the hunger connection is quite appropriate after all!

Legends and lore

Apatite is said to enhance one's insight, learning abilities and creativity, and to give increased self-confidence. It is also said to help achieve deeper states of meditation. Using Apatite is said to facilitate the desired results when working with other crystals.

Apatite is also believed by crystal healers to be useful in improving one's coordination and strengthening muscles, and helps suppress hunger and ease hypertension.

This stunningly eye-catching pendant contains a gorgeous sea green Apatite

15 oval cut Apatite gems make up this truly dramatic ring

Over 2ct of Madagascan Apatite are used to make this striking pendant

Just the facts

The largest Apatite deposits are associated with alkalic rocks.

Apatite is actually three different minerals depending on the predominance of either fluorine, chlorine or the hydroxyl group: Calcium (Fluoro, Chloro, Hydroxyl) Phosphate. These ions can freely substitute in the crystal lattice and all three are usually present in every specimen, although some specimens are almost 100% pure in one group.

The colour in Apatite is often due to the presence of rare earth elements. Discovered in Spain, Apatite is commonly called "Asparagus Stone" because of its similarity in colour to the vegetable. Cat's Eye Apatite gems are also known.

Recent finds of what is now widely referred to as Neon Apatite in Madagascar has added to the popularity of this gem. The neon ranges from a green to blue and exhibits excellent saturation.

APATITE:	Pleochroism
Locations:	Madagascar, Mozambique, Kenya, Brazil, Sri Lanka
Colours Found:	Green, yellow, blue, violet, yellow - green, neon
Typical Cuts:	Cabochon, Octagon
Family:	Apatite
Hardness:	5.00
Refractive Index:	1.63 - 1.64
Relative Density:	3.10 - 3.30

AQUAMARINE

The sheer beauty of Aquamarine, with its wonderful colour and fantastic clarity, makes it popular with both the collector and the wearer of fine jewellery. It will come as no surprise that the name is derived from the Latin words for water and sea.

Blue, the world's most popular colour, is famous for its calming effect and, out of all the blues available, none match the serenity found in Aquamarine. Aquamarine gemstones embody all that is natural. Aquamarine, the sparkling birthstone for March, ranges from pastel blue to light green, its passive tones reminiscent of an invigorating sea breeze.

The white gold setting perfectly complements the unusual cushion cut of this Aquamarine gem

Legends and lore

Since antiquity, Aquamarine has been seen as a gemstone of great vision, its crystals often being used as eyes in the creation of sculpted statues that symbolise power and wisdom. According to legend, any man or woman who set eyes on these statues became a person of great wisdom, harnessing the ability to see into the future.

This majestic looking necklace is made up of Aquamarine flawlessly paired with Diamonds

On occasions, these statues were placed in strategic positions near the coastline, where they could calm the wrath of the god Poseidon, thus insuring the safe return of those on ships at sea.

A rare Cat's Eye Aquamarine bordered with Tanzanite

Aquamarine has long been associated with its ability to capture oceanic energy. When amulets made of Aquamarine were worn, sailors believed that unmatched bravery would

Don Kogen, the Gem Hunter says:

"Although the deeper shades of blue are rarer and generally command higher prices, many prefer the oceanic hues of Brazilian Aquamarine as they provide a true reflection of the sea. Either way, the gentle lustre and delicate tones of Aquamarine are a majestic contribution to any gemstone collection."

be instilled in their souls. These fisherman's friends accompanied their owners while out on the high seas and, in the event of a storm, were tossed overboard to placate Poseidon's anger. Interestingly, Thai culture contains a common belief that Aquamarine can ward off seasickness and prevent wearers from drowning. Because of its association with the sea, Aquamarine is considered to be a gemstone of purification and cleansing that washes the mind with fresh clear thoughts and promotes self-expression.

Its calming effects make it a popular gemstone for those who practice meditation, as it is also believed to eradicate fears and phobias.

Just the facts

Aquamarine, symbolising the near perfect clarity and transparency of the ocean, is the big sister of the Beryl family whose relatives also include Bixbite, Goshenite, Emerald, Heliodor and Morganite.

Brazil has been the world's major supplier of Aquamarine for decades. The infamous Marambaia area is one of the most important sources of fine Aquamarine in the world.

Today, however, several African nations, including Nigeria, Mozambique, Zambia and Madagascar provide an equal, if not greater, supply of similarly beautiful examples. The different shades of Aquamarine are distinguished by their own names. "Santa Maria" is the name of the rare, intensely deep blue Aquamarine found in the Santa Maria de Itabira mines of Brazil. Very similar colours are also found in certain mines in Africa, especially in Mozambique, where they have come to be known as "Santa Maria Africana".

Another Brazilian beauty is the deep blue "Espirito Santo", coming from the Brazilian state of Espirito Santo. Yet another beautifully coloured variety has taken its name from a 1954 Brazilian beauty queen, "Martha Rocha".

AQUAMARINE

A beautifully hand-crafted pair of Mozambique Aquamarine earrings

A stunning full carat of Aquamarine set onto delicately detailed shoulders

AQUAMARINE:	March's birthstone
Locations:	Brazil, Madagascar, Mozambique, Zambia, Nigeria, Namibia, Tanzania
Colours Found:	Pastel blue to light green
Typical Cuts:	All cuts
Family:	Beryl
Hardness:	7.50 - 8.00
Refractive Index:	1.57 - 1.59
Relative Density:	2.68 - 2.80

AVENTURINE

Aventurine's name is derived from an accident. During the 18th Century, Venetian glass workers were preparing molten glass when copper filings accidentally fell into the batch, producing glass with sparkles. The name Aventurine comes from the Italian "a ventura" which means "by chance".

But make no mistake, Aventurine is certainly not glass, it is actually a much sought after member of the Chalcedony family.

A 4ct blue beauty set on over 7 grammes of 9k gold

The captivating blend of Moonstone and Blue Aventurine

A dazzling Green Aventurine bezel set into 7.4g of sterling silver

AVENTURINE:	Aventurescence
Locations:	India, Chile, Spain, Russia, Brazil, Austria, Tanzania
Colours Found:	Green, peach, brown, blue, creamy green
Typical Cuts:	Cabochons, beads, ornamentals
Family:	Quartz
Hardness:	6.50
Refractive Index:	1.54
Relative Density:	2.59 - 2.61

Legends and lore

Aventurine has been used as a lucky talisman and is a popular gem for gamblers.

Legends say that it is an all-purpose healer, used to reduce stress, develop confidence and imagination and improve prosperity. An ancient legend from Tibet tells of its use to help nearsightedness and to improve the wearer's creativity.

Many crystal healers believe that Aventurine has the capacity to calm a troubled spirit, balance emotions and bring an inner peace. It is also believed to enhance leadership qualities, allowing the wearer to act decisively, with strong intuitive power.

Just the facts

Aventurine is a Chalcedony that contains small inclusions of one of several shiny minerals which give the gem a glistening effect. The glistening effect of Aventurine is known as "Aventurescence". The colour of the Aventurescence depends on the mineral included in the gem. Mica inclusions give the gem a yellow or silver glitter or sheen. Goethite and Hematite inclusions give the gem a red or grey glitter or sheen. Fuschite inclusions give the gem a green sheen.

Aventurine ranges in colour from green, peach, brown, blue and creamy green. If a colour is not stated with the word Aventurine, it is usually assumed to be green. In the past, Green Aventurine has been miscalled "Indian Jade".

BERYL

The name Beryl is taken from the Ancient Greek "Beryllos" for their precious blue-green colour of sea water. This was originally applied to all green gemstones, but later used only for Beryl. Some scholars believe the word Beryl is related to the ancient trading city of Belur or perhaps came from the word pearl known as "Velurya" in old Hindi and "Vaidurya" in Sanskrit.

Beryl is, when absolutely pure, totally devoid of colour. Small amounts of metallic elements can be present in the crystal structure, giving rise to many magnificent colour variations. Emeralds (page 42), Aquamarines (page 20), Bixbite (page 24) are all members of the Beryl family.

19 prong set Yellow Beryl gems make up this extraordinary ring

Just the facts

Gemstone colour varieties that belong to the Beryl family with specific names are listed below.

Aquamarine	Pale green to blue
Emerald	Intense green
Iolite	Dark blue to grey
Heliodor	Pale yellow to yellowish-orange
Morganite	Pale pink to salmon coloured
Fire Beryl™ (Goshenite)	Colourless
Yellow Beryl	Strong yellow tones
Golden Beryl	Dark yellow to gold colour
Bixbite	Red to raspberry
White Beryl	Colourless

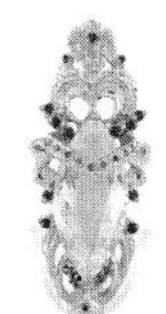

This extraordinary piece contains an impressive 8.6ct of colourless Goshenite

Beryls are famous for their perfect, six-sided prismatic hexagon crystals that usually occur individually. These are often enormous and some 30 foot (8 metre), well-crystallised examples are known to have existed.

All Beryl varieties are faceted into various gem cuts and some Beryls display phenomena including asterism (star effect), chatoyancy (cat's eye effect) and an unusual effect in Emerald, called trapichism.

More information can be found on individual members of the Beryl family throughout this guide.

BERYL:	Perfect, 6-sided prismatic hexagon crystals
Locations:	Brazil, South Africa, Afghanistan, Pakistan, Colombia, Madagascar, Nigeria, Mozambique, Zambia
Colours Found:	Blue-green, pale green to blue, intense green, pale yellow to yellowish-orange, pale pink to salmon, colourless, red to raspberry
Typical Cuts:	All cuts
Family:	Beryl
Hardness:	7.50 - 8.00
Refractive Index:	1.56 - 1.61
Relative Density:	2.60 - 2.90

BIXBITE *(PEZZOTTAITE)*

Bixbite is the variety name for the deep gooseberry pink to red variety of Beryl. Named after the mineral collector Maynard Bixby, Bixbite was discovered at the turn of the 20th Century in the Thomas Range, Utah. Bixbite is commonly called Red Emerald and very occasionally referred to as American Emerald.

Very rare in nature, Bixbite is known to occur in only a few localities in the Western United States, possibly one location in Mexico, Madagascar and possibly Brazil. Material that is suitable for faceting is rare and the largest gemstones are typically less than 2 carats in size.

Octagonal cut Bixbite superbly set into 18k gold decorated with a traditional two-tone design

The 18k white gold surrounding this rare Cat's Eye Bixbite dramatically enhances the lustre of the gem

Just the facts

The "traditional" main source for Bixbite (the Wah Wah Mountains deposit in Utah) has presently ceased operation.

In 2002, Bixbite was discovered in Southern Madagascar. This deposit yielded some extremely rare larger crystals but it is now depleted and mining from this location has ceased. Bixbite from Madagascar is also known as Pezzottaite in reference to its slightly different crystallography (trigonal versus hexagonal). The name Madagascan Raspberyl has also been utilised at gem shows but only in combination with Pezzottaite.

Even more than Emerald, inclusions in Bixbite are common, especially in the larger carat weights. However, Bixbite's rarity and novelty for gemstone collectors has always been the primary factor in its high valuations rather than its aesthetic beauty.

Bixbite has all the qualities a gem needs for beauty, durability and rarity. Rarer than Ruby, Bixbite is not likely to show up on your best friend's finger!

BIXBITE:	Monoclonic crystals
Locations:	U. S. A, Mexico, Madagascar, Brazil
Colours Found:	Deep gooseberry pink to red
Typical Cuts:	Cabochons, oval, hexagon
Family:	Beryl
Hardness:	7.50 - 8.00
Refractive Index:	1.57 - 1.60
Relative Density:	2.66 - 2.70

What our Craftsmen say:

Mrs.Chatchada Sutiphum - Polishing

"This is a gem that gets all of the girls talking here in Thailand. It is simply one of the most feminine of colours and often has a beauty that can mesmerise."

CASSITERITE

Cassiterite's name comes from the Phoenician word for tin "Cassiterid" (Greek equivalent: "Kassiteros"), which referred generically to the islands of England and Ireland.

In fact, around the 6th Century BC, Carthage (the greatest Phoenician colony) tried to rule the tin monopoly by importing tin ores directly from the original areas of extraction, the "Tin Islands" (i.e. Cassiterid islands) known today as England.

Just the facts

The primary ore of Tin, most sources of Cassiterite today are not primary deposits but alluvial deposits (see page 161 for mining techniques).

Cassiterite has been an important tin ore for eons and is still the greatest source of tin today. During the Bronze Age it was added to molten copper to form bronze.

Some of the oldest Cassiterite mines, such as those in Cornwall, England have been worked since 2000 BC and are now completely exhausted.

But this multifunctional ore is much more than just an industrial mineral. Some rarer examples of Cassiterite are definitely of gem quality (i.e. rare, beautiful and durable).

To discover the true beauty of this gem, the rough material needs polishing. Once this is completed, Cassiterite displays a high lustre which, in combination with its multiple crystal faces, produces stunning brilliance.

Large cut Cassiterites of more than one carat are exceedingly rare. Common colours include black, reddish brown and yellow.

Cassiterite is found in Boliva, China, Indonesia, Malaysia, Mexico, Namibia, Russia and Spain.

If you are looking for a piece of historical England to proudly adorn your body, then Cassiterite must surely be a first choice. Having said that, it has also been found in alluvial deposits in Wales.

The precision faceting on this trilliant cut gem enhances its inner fire

A striking 7.4cts of Cassiterite in an 18k setting

Victoria Burton
Gems TV Presenter

"All items of jewellery shown in this guide were crafted by Gems TV during 2005 and were sold direct to the public. The average selling price was amazingly under £65!

During 2006 we anticipate introducing a further 22,700 individual designs, featuring approximately 490 different gem types."

CASSITERITE:	Greatest source of tin
Locations:	Boliva, China, Indonesia, Malaysia, Mexico, Namibia, Russia, Spain
Colours Found:	Black, reddish brown, yellow
Typical Cuts:	All cuts
Family:	Rutile
Hardness:	6.00 - 7.00
Refractive Index:	2.00
Relative Density:	6.60 - 7.00

CHALCEDONY

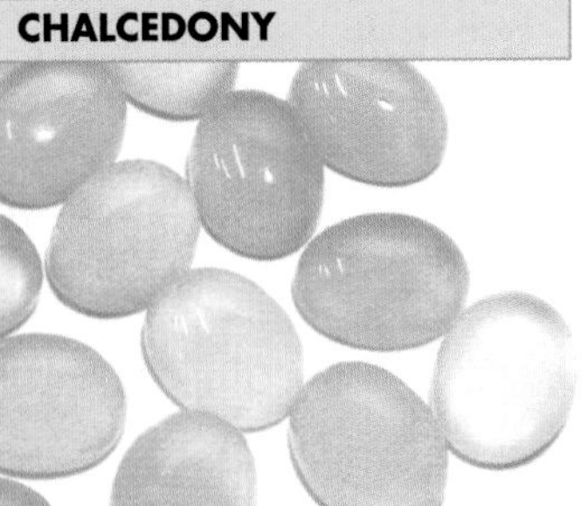

Chalcedony's name is derived from Chalcedon or Calchedon, an ancient port of Bithynia, near present day Istanbul, Turkey. It has a waxy lustre and appears in a great variety of colours usually blue, white, buff, tan, green, red, grey, black, yellow or brown. Different coloured varieties of Chalcedony have individual names.

Chalcedony	Blue to brownish blue
Agate	Red to reddish brown
Sard	Light to dark brown
Chrysoprase	Apple green
Bloodstone	Green with red spots
Jasper	Red, Yellow, Brown, Green (Generally has spots)
Flint	Dull grey to black

A striking 8.6ct icy blue Chalcedony gem sits regally on the delicate shoulders of this ring

This stylishly simple pendant shows the versatility of Chalcedony gemstones

Legends and lore

Chalcedony was used during the Renaissance as a magic amulet to promote health and safety.

The earliest recorded use of Chalcedony was for projectile points, knives, tools, and containers such as cups and bowls.

The Romans prized Chalcedony as seals and, in the New Testament (Revelations 21:19), Chalcedony is one of the twelve gemstones set in the foundations of the city walls of Jerusalem. As compiled by Andreas, Bishop of Caesurae, one of the earliest writers to tie the Apostles with the symbolism of the twelve gems of Jerusalem, Chalcedony was for the Apostle St. Andrew.

CHALCEDONY:	Waxy lustre
Locations:	Madagascar, Tanzania, South Africa, India, Brazil, Mexico, U.S.A
Colours Found:	Blue, white, buff, tan, green, red, grey, black, yellow, brown
Typical Cuts:	Cabochon
Family:	Quartz
Hardness:	6.50
Refractive Index:	1.54
Relative Density:	2.58 - 2.64

Just the facts

Chalcedony is one of the gemstones used in Commesso or Florentine mosaic. Developed in Florence in the late 16th Century, Commesso is a technique of fashioning pictures with thin, cut-to-shape pieces of brightly coloured, semiprecious gems.

Normally faceted as a cabochon it is often used to great effect in both necklaces and bracelets.

CHRYSOBERYL

The gem of springtime, youth and innocence, the name Chrysoberyl is derived from the Greek for golden "Chryso" and green gemstone "Beryl".

Its rarest variety, Alexandrite, is quite well known, although the number of people who have heard of Alexandrite is probably 100 times greater than the number who have ever seen one, and 1,000 times greater than the number who have ever owned one.

Legends and lore

Said to bring peace of mind and increase self-confidence, Chrysoberyl also promotes kindness, generosity, benevolence, hope, optimism, renewal, new beginnings, compassion and forgiveness.

Bezel set Chrysoberyl gems in an effortlessly graceful piece

Just the facts

When cut, Chrysoberyl is an extremely brilliant gem, ideal for everyday wear and is rapidly gaining popularity.

Ordinary transparent Chrysoberyl is most often yellow, yellowish green or brown in colour. The most desired gems are brilliant yellows, greens and occasionally oranges.

This mysteriously captivating bracelet is made up of 26 beautifully cut gems

The colour in Yellow Chrysoberyl is due to iron ($Fe+3$) impurities.

Cat's Eye Chrysoberyl is a translucent gem ranging in colour from a honey yellow or honey brown to yellowish green to an apple green. It is known for its reflected light effect called "chatoyancy." This is achieved by cutting gems that have very small, parallel "Silk" inclusions into cabochons. As the gem is rotated, it exhibits a distinct, silvery white line across its dome that seems to open and close like a cat's eye.

CHRYSOBERYL:	Chatoyancy, cyclic twins crystals
Locations:	Zimbabwe, Tanzania, Madagascar, Zambia, Brazil, India, Sri Lanka, Russia
Colours Found:	Yellow, yellowish green, brown
Typical Cuts:	Cabochon, pear, oval, beads
Family:	Chrysoberyl
Hardness:	8.00 - 8.50
Refractive Index:	1.74 - 1.75
Relative Density:	3.50 - 3.80

What our Craftsmen say:

Mr.Satcha Limcharoen - Jeweller

"If Alexandrite falls outside of your budget or when it is in short supply Chrysoberyl, being from the same family, can be a great substitute."

CHRYSOPRASE

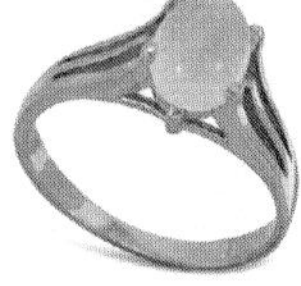

An Australian Chrysoprase prong set into this vividly stunning piece

Emerald Green Chrysoprase perfectly complemented by 9k white gold

Fashion at its best with this Australian Chrysoprase

CHRYSOPRASE:	Mentioned in the Bible
Locations:	Brazil, Russia, Madagascar, South Africa, Australia, Czech Republic, U.S.A
Colours Found:	Apple green
Typical Cuts:	Cabochons, beads, cameos
Family:	Chalcedony
Hardness:	6.50
Refractive Index:	1.54
Relative Density:	2.58 - 2.64

Also colloquially known as Cat's Eye or Australian Jade, its name comes from the Greek words "Chrysos" meaning gold and "Prason" meaning leek, due to its colour similarities with the vegetable.

The most valuable variety of Chalcedony, Chrysoprase is prized for its colour and rarity. Chrysoprase is an opalescent apple green coloured variety of Chalcedony Quartz.

Legends and lore

Chrysoprase is believed by crystal healers to increase grace and inner equilibrium.

Chrysoprase was used by the Greeks, Romans and Egyptians in jewellery and other ornamental objects. In ancient Egyptian jewellery, Chrysoprase was often set next to Lapis Lazuli.

Chrysoprase is mentioned in the Bible as being one of the twelve gemstones set in the foundations of the city walls of Jerusalem (Revelations 21:19).

Chrysoprase was very popular in the 14th Century when the Holy Roman Emperor Charles IV used it to decorate chapels, including the Chapel of Saint Wencelsas in Prague.

Chrysoprase was also a favourite gem of Frederick the Great of Prussia and Queen Anne of England.

Just the facts

Chrysoprase can vary in colour from yellowish green to apple green and grass green, depending on the levels of hydrated silicates and nickel oxides present in the gem.

Because of its semi-opaque green colour, Chrysoprase was often mistaken for Imperial Jade.

Other green Chalcedonys include Prase (a very rare less vivid green Chalecedony found in Eastern Europe and Delaware & Pennsylvania, U.S.A.) and Mtorolite (a variety of green Chalcedony coloured by Chromium found in Zimbabwe).

CITRINE

Citrine is a golden yellow form of Quartz that takes its name from "Citron", the French word for lemon. Citrine is a beautiful, translucent gem and is one of November's birthstones.

Legends and lore

In former times, Citrine was used as a protective talisman against the plague, bad skin and evil thoughts.

Citrine promotes creativity, helps personal clarity and eliminates self-destructive tendencies. Citrine was commonly used as a charm against snakebites and other venomous reptiles.

Amongst its many medicinal uses, Citrine is believed to aid digestion, remove toxins from the body and be useful in the treatment of depression, constipation and diabetes.

The first occurrences of Citrine being utilised by man were in Greece, in the Hellenistic period (end of the 4th to the end of the 1st Century BC).

The first use of Citrine by the Romans was in intaglios and cabochon cuts in the first centuries after the birth of Christ.

The remarkable facets of this Citrine gem emphasise the expertise of our highly skilled gem cutters

This eye-catching piece contains 5 Citrine gems brilliantly accentuated by pave set Diamonds

Just the facts

Citrine occurs naturally in proximity to Amethyst and is a related mineral.

Citrine, like Amethyst, is a form of Quartz.

Colours range from pale yellow to yellowish-brown and "Madeira" red, after the colour of the wine. The yellow colour is from the presence of iron. The darker the colour, the higher the grade.

Brazilian Citrine at its best in these subtly beautiful earrings

Traditionally, the "Madeira" shades were valued more highly but these days many people prefer Citrine's brighter lemon tones.

Most of the high-grade Citrine mined today comes from Uruguay, Brazil and many African nations. Natural Citrine can also be found in the Ural Mountains of Russia, in Dauphine, France, and in Madagascar.

Citrine can be easily confused with Topaz and has even been called "Topaz Quartz".

CITRINE

This impressive piece includes a 9.9ct Citrine with 10 Diamonds set into the shoulders

A faultless blend of Citrine and Diamonds

A uniquely cut prong set Citrine gives this pendant its contemporary feel

CITRINE:	November's birthstone
Locations:	Madagascar, Brazil, Zambia, France, Russia
Colours Found:	Golden yellow
Typical Cuts:	All cuts
Family:	Quartz
Hardness:	7.00
Refractive Index:	1.50
Relative Density:	2.60 - 2.70

Gems TV presenter & gem expert Paul Bridges says:

"To look into the window of a clear Citrine is to see into the heart of nature's colourful canvas. The oranges, lemons and limes of Citrine are reminiscent of the morning light in a quiet Mediterranean village. Perhaps nature first practised painting the fruits of our earth before slowly perfecting her touch by skillfully colouring an occasional Quartz. For Citrine, the rarest member of the Quartz family of gemstones, explodes with the radiance of nature's brightest star, the Sun. Teaming with warm, glowing colour, Citrine might be the gemstone choice of a child, whose vitality and youth is drawn to the splendour of a gemstone sure to provide a playground of natural beauty to any beholder.

As with all her finest masterpieces, to Citrine, nature has added her brushstrokes over thousands of years. Her care and attention to detail has yielded a gemstone which has been revered throughout the ages. Enjoyed by the Romans, treasured by the Elizabethans and particularly popular during the 19th Century, Citrine is, today, welcoming the dawn of yet another popularity renaissance. Since becoming the favoured gemstone of Hollywood's golden-age stars like Greta Garbo and Joan Crawford, Citrine now finds itself at the forefront of contemporary culture, adorning the high fashion of catwalk models and the gemstone jewellery of celebrities.

Today, Hollywood stars such as Gwyneth Paltrow, Cate Blanchett, Drew Barrymore, Nicole Kidman and Claire Danes are abandoning diamond studs, preferring the adornment of distinctively coloured gemstones, including Citrine. The attraction is easy to see, for Citrine not only brightens jewellery, but blends especially well with the yellow gleam of polished gold.

Indeed, Citrine is now so popular among the Hollywood set that, in 2003, a new restaurant, called Citrine, opened on Melrose Avenue in West Hollywood. Like the gemstone, it has quickly come of age to establish itself as a firm favourite of Hollywood's elite.

Once the treasured possession of emperors, kings and queens, today the golden honey colours of Citrine are to be enjoyed not only by royalty, but also by Hollywood stars - and, now, most of all, by you!"

CORNELIAN

Also known as Sadoine or Mecca Stone, and sometimes spelt Carnelian, the name is derived from the Latin world for flesh, "Carne", due to the colouring of the gem.

Cornelian is a translucent orange to red variety of Chalcedony. A uniformly coloured Cryptocrystalline Quartz, its red tints are caused by iron oxide impurities.

Legends and lore

A deeply religious gem, Cornelian was used by the Egyptian goddess, Isis, to protect the dead on their journey through the afterlife.

Cornelian is mentioned in the Bible as being one of the "Stones of Fire" (Ezekiel 28:13-16) given to Moses that featured in the breastplate of his brother and high priest Aaron (Exodus 28:15-30) and is also one of the twelve gemstones set in the foundations of the city walls of Jerusalem (Revelations 21:19). As compiled by Andreas, Bishop of Caesurae, one of the earliest writers to tie the Apostles with the symbolism of the twelve gems of Jerusalem, it is the symbol of the Apostle Philip.

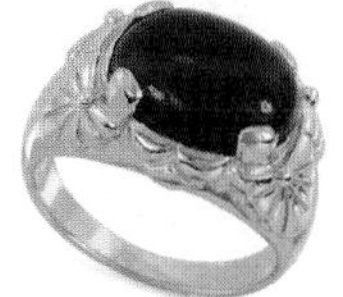

The 9k gold setting highlights the fiery red colour of this Brazilian Cornelian

To this day, Buddhists in China, India and Tibet believe in the protective powers of Cornelian and often follow the Egyptian practice of setting the gem with Turquoise and Lapis Lazuli for enhanced power.

An unusual Madagascan Cornelian Cameo pendant

Cornelian has been recommended for those with bad memories, creative blocks, befuddled minds, weak voices and a lack of courage. It is said to be beneficial in treating impotence, infertility, insomnia, menstrual cramps, neuralgia, rheumatism, asthma, bad blood, lethargy, digestive problems and skin conditions like acne and psoriasis in both humans and animals.

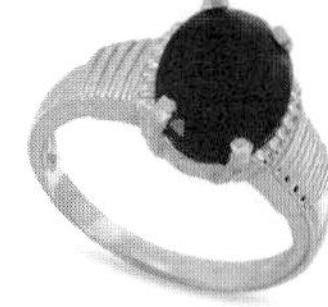

Our designers take inspiration from all over the world

What our Craftsmen say:

Miss Alisa Klahan - Quality Assurance

"When our gem hunters are able to acquire Cornelian there is a rush of excitement in the design centre. Everyone at Gems TV loves working with this gem."

CORNELIAN:	Translucent
Locations:	Madagascar, India, Brazil, Sri Lanka, Uruguay, U.S.A
Colours Found:	Orange to red
Typical Cuts:	Cabochons, beads, cameos
Family:	Chalcedony
Hardness:	7.00
Refractive Index:	2.65 - 2.66
Relative Density:	1.543 -1.554

DANBURITE

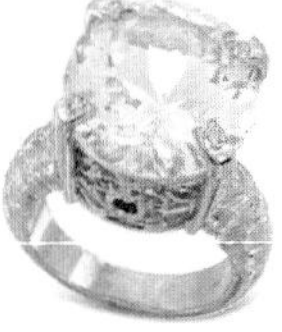

This immense piece of jewellery is made up of over 11ct of Danburite

A combination of Mexican Danburite and Chrome Tourmaline gives this piece its feminine beauty

This stunning colourless piece of Danburite is cushion cut to enhance its inner brilliance

DANBURITE:	Excellent natural Diamond alternative
Locations:	Madagascar, Maxico, U.S. A, Japan, Switzerland, Germany
Colours Found:	Clear or white, but shades of yellow, pink, brown
Typical Cuts:	Round, oval, princess, trilliant, fancy
Family:	Danburite
Hardness:	7.00 - 7.50
Refractive Index:	1.63 - 1.64
Relative Density:	2.97 - 3.02

Danburite, discovered in 1839, is named after Danbury, Connecticut, where it first was unearthed. Interestingly, the original deposits are now inaccessible as they lie under a major metropolitan area!

Danburite is a relatively new gemstone in today's jewellery world but is rapidly growing in popularity. An excellent natural Diamond alternative, Danburite also has similarities with White Topaz.

Legends and lore

It is believed that Danburite aids with communication and relationships with others, and helps to remove toxins from the body. Metaphysically, Danburite is believed to be a powerful intellectual activator and an excellent healing tool.

Just the facts

Danburite are rare crystals of Calcium Boron Silicate (CaB2Si2O8), the best of which are usually found in Mexico. Danburite is also found in Japan, Madagascar, Mexico, Switzerland, Germany and U.S.A.

Visually, Danburites make an excellent natural gemstone alternative to Diamonds, and harmonise with almost every fashion accessory.

Fine quality Danburites are clear or white, but shades of yellow, pink and brown can also be found. Although most Danburites are greyish and opaque, some are clear and colourless, or a very light pink, with striated sides and chisel-like terminations.

Clarity should be transparent to translucent with a vitreous lustre.

With a hardness of 7, they wear well and are stunningly beautiful when faceted and set in rings and pendants.

Don Kogen, the Gem Hunter says:

"Keep your eyes on this one, we are desperately hunting for more and believe it should become famous."

DIAMOND

The word Diamond comes from the Greek word "Adamas" meaning unconquerable or invincible.

"Diamonds are Forever", sang Shirley Bassey, while Marilyn insisted they were "A Girl's Best Friend". Celebrated in song, Diamond, April's birthstone, has over the last century become the most marketed of gemstones.

Legends and lore

The myths and facts associated with the Diamond transcends cultures and continents.

The world's first known reference to this gemstone comes from an Indian Sanskrit manuscript, the Arthsastra (which translates as "The Lesson of Profit") written by Kautiliya, a minister to Chandragupta, of the Mauryan Dynasty (322 BC – 185 BC).

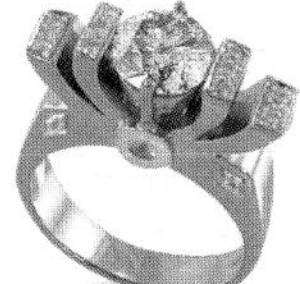

The distinctive design of this piece is matched only by the arresting beauty of the Diamonds

Plato wrote about Diamonds as living beings, embodying celestial spirits.

Roman literature makes its first distinct mention of Diamonds only in the 1st Century AD, in reference to the alluvial Diamonds found in India and Borneo.

8 delicate bezel set Diamonds encircle the centre gem

The ancient Greeks and Romans believed they were tears of the gods and splinters from falling stars. Cupid's arrows were supposed to be tipped with Diamonds, having thus a magic that nothing else could equal.

The Hindus believed that they were created when bolts of lightning struck rocks. They even placed Diamonds in the eyes of some of their statues.

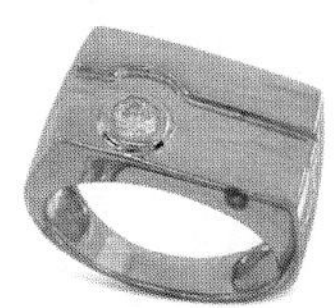

A stylish example of Diamonds in a gentlemen's ring.

Jewish high priests turned to Diamonds to decide the innocence or guilt of the accused. A Diamond held before a guilty person was supposed to dull and darken, while a Diamond held before an innocent person glowed with increasing brilliance.

The Romans wore Diamonds because they were thought to possess broad magical powers over life's troubles, being able in particular to give to the wearer strength, invincibility, bravery and courage during battle.

This vintage looking piece is made up of African Diamond and two tone 14k gold

DIAMOND

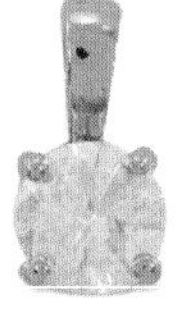

A simple yet glamourous Diamond pendant

Sophistication in jewellery made up of 20 brilliant cut Diamonds

Double rings containing the timeless pairing of Diamonds and 9k yellow gold

Steve Ashton
Gems TV Presenter

"All items of jewellery shown in this guide were crafted by Gems TV during 2005 and were sold direct to the public. The average selling price was amazingly under £65!

During 2006 we anticipate introducing a further 22,700 individual designs, featuring approximately 490 different gem types."

Kings, in olden days, led the battles on the battlefields wearing heavy leather breastplates studded with Diamonds and other precious gems, because it was believed that Diamonds possessed God-given magical qualities and powers far beyond the understanding of common man. Thus, warriors stayed clear of Kings and those who were fortunate enough to have the magical Diamonds in their breastplates.

An act of Louis IX of France (1214-1270) that established a sumptuary law reserving Diamonds for the king, indicates the rarity of this gem and the value conferred on it at that time.

Until the 14th Century, only kings could wear Diamonds, because they stood for strength, courage and invincibility. Small numbers of Diamonds began appearing in the 14th Century in European regalia and jewellery, set mainly as an accent point amongst pearls. But the possession of extraordinarily large and noble Diamonds was always the privilege of royal houses and particularly rich families. As an example, the imperial crown of the Russian Czarina Catherine the Second (1729-1796) was mounted with 4,936 sparkling Diamonds.

In the Middle Ages and the Renaissance, every ring set with a precious gem was not considered as much a piece of jewellery, as an amulet that bestowed magical powers upon its wearer. When set in gold and worn on the left side, it was believed that Diamonds held the power to drive away nightmares, ward off devils and phantoms and soothe savage beasts. A house or garden touched at each corner with a Diamond was supposed to be protected from lightning, storms and blight. Diamonds were also supposed to impart virtue and generosity, calm the mentally ill and even determine lawsuits in the wearer's favour.

Not only was it commonly believed that Diamonds could bring luck and success, but also that they could counter the effects of astrological events.

Just the facts

You may have heard about the 4 Cs related to valuing gemstones and in particular, Diamonds. While other factors such as origin sometimes need to be taken into consideration when valuing coloured gemstones, below is a basic guide to the 4 Cs that gemstone professionals and connoisseurs the world over rely on - colour, cut, carat weight and clarity.

Colour

Colourless and near-colourless Diamonds are rare, beautiful and highly prized amongst connoisseurs. To the untrained eye, most Diamonds look white. However, to the professional and the collector, there are small differences in the degrees of whiteness seen.

An example of the versatility of Diamonds in this set containing earrings, a ring and a pendant

Cut

With round brilliant cut Diamonds accounting for over 80% of Diamond sales worldwide, ask someone "What shape is a Diamond?" and they will probably say round. Despite this figure, there are many other beautiful Diamond cuts that warrant serious consideration. The eight most popular Diamond cuts are emerald cut, heart cut, marquise cut, oval cut, round brilliant cut, pear cut, princess cut and radiant cut.

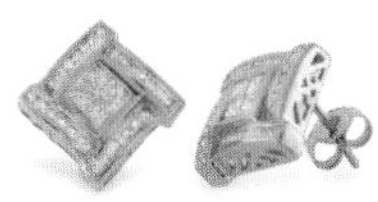

Channel set Diamonds give these earrings a contemporary elegance

Unlike coloured gemstones, Diamonds are cut, shaped and proportioned to a remarkably uniform ideal. In 1919, Marcel Tolkowsky published his opinions on what Diamond proportions result in the optimum balance of brilliance and fire. Diamond graders do take these proportions into account when evaluating the worth of a Diamond.

The stylish and glamourous blend of 9k white gold and sparkling Diamonds

Carat weight

As mentioned above, unlike gemstones, Diamonds are cut to a uniform ideal for maximum brilliance, sparkle and fire. With this uniform cutting and proportions, we can very conveniently and accurately equate Diamond carat size with their millimetre size.

A contemporary Asian pendant

DIAMOND

Effortless elegance in this simplistic Black Diamond piece

Brilliant cut earrings containing two 1.8ct Black Diamonds

5 Black Diamonds in a modern square prong setting

Delicate sophistication in this blend of Black Diamond and yellow gold

Round Brilliant Cut Diamond	
1 mm	0.01 Ct
2 mm	0.03 Ct
3 mm	0.10 Ct
4 mm	0.25 Ct
5 mm	0.50 Ct
6 mm	0.75 Ct
6.5 mm	1.00 Ct
7 mm	1.25 Ct
7.5 mm	1.65 Ct

Clarity

Inclusions are tiny natural features within the body of a Diamond. Nearly all gemstones contain some inclusions, however, many are microscopic and can only be glimpsed under magnification. If inclusions do not interfere with the brilliance, sparkle and fire seen by the passage of light through the gem, they do not affect the beauty or value.

The GIA Diamond grading system

Developed by the GIA (Gemological Institute of America), this system is now commonplace for the retailing of Diamonds across the globe and consists of a Diamond Clarity Scale and a Diamond Colour Scale.

GIA Diamond clarity scale

(FL) FLAWLESS: Shows no inclusions or blemishes of any sort under 10X magnification when observed by an experienced grader.

(IF) INTERNALLY FLAWLESS: Has no inclusions when examined by an experienced grader using 10X magnification, but will have some minor surface blemishes.

(VVS1 and VVS2) VERY VERY SLIGHTLY INCLUDED: Contains minute inclusions that are difficult even for experienced graders to see under 10X magnification.

(VS1 and VS2) VERY SLIGHTLY INCLUDED: Contains minute inclusions such as small crystals, clouds or feathers when observed with effort under 10X magnification.

(SI1 and SI2) SLIGHTLY INCLUDED: Contains inclusions (clouds, included crystals, knots, cavities and feathers) that are noticeable to an experienced grader under 10X magnification.

In addition to SI1 and SI2, the SI3 Diamond clarity grade was created because many in the Diamond industry felt that there was too wide a gap between SI2 and I1. Shortly after the European Gemological Laboratory (EGL) started issuing certificates with the SI3 grade, the Rapaport Diamond Report added SI3 to its price list (the Rapaport Diamond Report or Rap Sheet is the definitive price guide for Diamonds and is widely used by both jewellery manufacturers and Diamond wholesalers). Despite its widespread acceptance in the industry, the GIA surprisingly still does not recognise SI3 grades!

(I1, I2, I3) INCLUDED: Contains inclusions (possibly large feathers or large included crystals) that are obvious under 10X magnification.

(PK) PIQUE: Inclusions easily visible to the naked eye.

19 pave set Pink Diamonds in the contemporary square centre area

GIA Diamond colour scale

Prior to the introduction of the GIA grading system, the letters A, B & C were used to grade Diamonds. As the GIA wanted a fresh start, they decided to begin with the letter D.

D, E, F. These purest tints are rare and comparatively expensive. Their rare colour assigns them a higher market price.

G, H, I. Often offering much better value, to the untrained eye they seem the exact same colour as the more expensive D, E and F colours.

J, K, L. Discounted for their barely perceivable yellowish tints, Diamonds in this range offer excellent value.

M - Z. Further discounted for their more distinct yellow hues. Diamonds outside the normal colour range are called fancy-colours and come in about any colour you can imagine (pink, red, green, purple, black, blue, yellow and more).

This Icy Blue Diamond sits perfectly in 9k white gold

3 Deep Blue Diamonds perfectly complemented by 9k white gold

DIAMOND

A stylishly simple pendant featuring a stunning Champagne Diamond

A strikingly modest bezel set Champagne Diamond

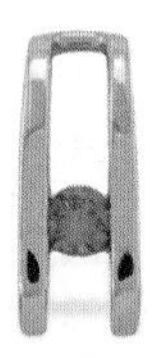

A contemporary tension set 1/4ct Blue Diamond

DIAMOND:	April's birthstone
Locations:	Africa
Colours Found:	Colourless, fancy colours
Typical Cuts:	Round brilliant, princess
Family:	Carbon
Hardness:	10.00
Refractive Index:	2.41
Relative Density:	3.50

Pairs and suites

Pairs or Suites of Diamonds matched for colour, clarity and cut are more highly valued per carat or per gem than single Diamonds of the same quality. Given the rarity of many Diamonds, a matching set is disproportionately hard to find and thus commands a higher per carat price than if each of the Diamonds from the suite were sold separately.

Coloured Diamonds

Most Coloured Diamonds found in jewellery today are normally treated. The process known as Colour Enhancement involves using clean Diamonds and modifying their colour with a combination of electron bombardment and heat, using safe electron-accelerator technology. This process exactly duplicates the "natural process" a Diamond undergoes during its formation. All the Colour Enhanced Diamonds sold by Gems TV are treated in the U.S. to certified international standards.

Unlike some other Diamond treatments, Colour Enhanced Diamonds are treated to fulfil preferences for vivid colour only; this colouring technique does not try to hide or dissipate flaws. The myriad of popular Diamond colours produced using this technology includes blue, green, red, orange, yellow, pink, purple and black. The real beauty and popularity of these Diamonds lies in the fact that they combine the rich colour hues of coloured gems such as Rubies and Sapphires with the unforgettable brilliance and sparkle of a Diamond. In other words, they virtually become "two gems in one".

DIOPSIDE

Diopside was named in 1800 from the Greek word "Dis" meaning double and "Opsis" meaning vision, in reference to the Pleochroism (i.e. different colours are displayed when viewed from different angles) found in its prismatic form.

Legends & Lore

Diopside is also called the "Crying Gemstone", because it is believed by crystal healers to heal trauma, by bringing forth cleansing tears.

Diopside is assumed to bring creativity to the wearer and is said to be related to love and commitment. Crystal healers believe that, when worn close to the chest (such as in a pendant), Diopside can benefit the heart, lungs and circulation.

As green is frequently the colour of both Diopside and money, it has long been associated with wealth.

Many people within the industry feel that Diopside should be added to the Birthstone chart for the month of May.

Just the facts

Diopside is a Calcium Magnesium Silicate found in metamorphosed impure limestone, meteorites and igneous basalts. Diopside has been previously named Schefferite, White Schefferite and Zinc-Schefferite.

Diopside is the Magnesium rich member of the "Monoclinic-Pyroxene Series" that occurs when ions (and Magnesium) freely substitute each other.

Diopside crystals have a perfect cleavage in two directions, are often twinned and are short and columnar, but with an uneven fracture. Mineralogists easily recognise Diopside in the field by its crystals, its colour, its fracture, its cleavage and its white or white-green streak.

Diopside is typically white, blue, purple, brown, green, colourless and grey with a glassy lustre. The less common shades are yellowish brown and greenish brown.

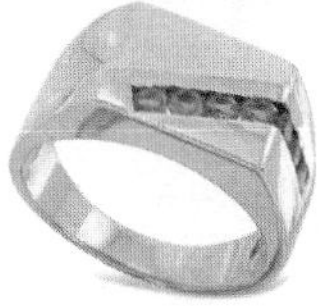

Russian Chrome Diopside in a contemporary example of gentlemen's jewellery

An arresting Chrome Diopside surrounded by 10 single prong set Diamonds

6 Marquise cut Chrome Diopside gems are used to create this extraordinary example of handcrafted jewellery

Rod Jinks
Gems TV Presenter

"All items of jewellery shown in this guide were crafted by Gems TV during 2005 and were sold direct to the public. The average selling price was amazingly under £65!

During 2006 we anticipate introducing a further 22,700 individual designs, featuring approximately 490 different gem types."

DIOPSIDE

Varieties of Diopside include "Chrome Diopside" (a Chromium-rich Diopside known for its deep green colour), "Violan" (a rare blue variety found in Italy), "Cat's Eye Diopside" (green with the effect due to inclusions of rutile needles), "Malacolite" (a white coloured variety), "Salaite" (an iron variety), "Dekalbite" (an iron free variety) and "Star Diopside" (a star with four rays).

Gem quality Diopsides are mined in Siberia, Italy, Sri Lanka, Brazil, Madagascar, South Africa and Pakistan. Uzbekistan, located between Tajikistan and Turkmenistan, is becoming an important locality for a variety of Chrome Diopside called Tashmarine. This variety has a slightly lower Chromium content than the Siberian material, a less saturated colour and can display grey or brown tones. India has the largest deposits of phenomenal Diopsides such as Cat's Eye Diopsides or Star Diopsides. The colour of African Diopside tends to be a more yellowish colour similar to Peridot.

These modern oval cut Diopside gems sit below four prong set Diamonds

Chrome Diopside

To most people, it sounds more like a car polish than a gemstone. But don't jump to any conclusions! Chrome Diopside has a beautiful rich green colour, similar to that of the best Emeralds or the rarest Tsavorite Garnets.

The dispersion of light inside this Chrome Diopside gem results in the emerald green colour

Coloured by Chromium, Chrome Diopside is also known as Russian Diopside. While there is little historical information regarding this rare gem type, some claim it is beneficial for health, relationships, spirituality and financial success.

A brilliant example of how our designers draw inspiration from everyday life to create our unique pieces

One major reason Chrome Diopside has been overlooked is that it has only recently become available in sizable commercial quantities, but now that it is available maybe it's time to change this beautiful gemstone's name. Interestingly, a company recently trademarked the name "Vertelite" for Russian Chrome Diopside. The name was created from "Verte" the Latin root word for green and "Lite" the Latin root word for tone.

Chrome Diopside displays strong birefringence and has a vitreous lustre. It is mostly available in small sizes, with large carat weights hard to find.

Chrome Diopside is mostly mined in Yakutia, Siberia. Yakutia territory is located in the extreme north of Asia and is considered the coldest place in Siberia as well as in the northern hemisphere. Mining is limited due to cold winters lasting for nine months; hence this gem is very seasonal and it has been difficult to maintain steady supply levels throughout the year.

Interestingly, Yakutia is also the source of 99% of all Russian Diamonds. Chrome Diopside, which is a Diamond mine indicator mineral, is sometimes found as an inclusion inside gem-quality Diamonds.

The liberalisation of the economy of the former Soviet Union has now made Chrome Diopside more available than ever before.

Star Diopside

Star Diopside is also known as "Black Star Diopside" because of its black or brown colour. asterism or the star effect is a reflection effect that appears as two or more intersecting bands of light across the surface of a gem.

Star Diopside has four rays, two of which are straight, while the other two are not at right angles to the first pair.

Star Diopside is mainly mined in India and is generally of a black or blackish green colour.

Cat's Eye Diopside

A green variety of Diopside, chatoyancy or the cat's eye effect is a reflection effect that appears as a single bright band of light across the surface of a gemstone. Cat's Eye Diopside is mainly mined in India.

Violan Diopside

Violan is light blue to purple in colour due to the presence of high amounts of Manganese. Violan is mainly mined in Italy.

DIOPSIDE

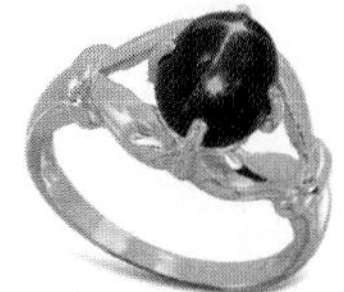

This Star Diopside ring is a flawless example of chatoyancy

This multigem ring shows that Diopside works as a great centre piece

9 square channel set Diopside gems give this ring a futuristic glamour

DIOPSIDE:	Perfect cleavage in two directions
Locations:	Russia, India, Italy, Siberia, Sri Lanka, Brazil, Madagascar, South Africa , Pakistan
Colours Found:	White, blue, purple, brown, green, colourless, grey
Typical Cuts:	Cushion, cabochon
Family:	Pyroxene
Hardness:	5.00 - 6.00
Refractive Index:	1.66 - 1.72
Relative Density:	3.20 - 3.60

EMERALD

For more than 4,000 years, the deep "Green Fire" of Emeralds has been treasured as a symbol of eternal spring and immortality. Shrouded in myth and lore, the birthstone for May isn't just a beautiful gem, Emeralds are also ornaments of power and politics that have created legends and moulded world history.

Prized by Egyptians, Romans, Aztecs, Crowned Heads of Europe and, today, gem connoisseurs the world over, Emeralds, more than any other precious gemstone have sparked the eternal fires of our collective imagination.

Legends and lore

Spring is a time of growth and rejuvenation. Nothing reflects this more than the intense green shades of Emeralds, May's birthstone.

Emeralds are regarded by many cultures as a symbol of personal development. It was once thought that Emeralds possessed the power to soothe the soul and sharpen wit.

Some people believe that wearing an Emerald brings wisdom, growth and patience. And, as any couple would agree, all of these qualities are essential for lasting love. This may explain why a gift of Emerald is considered symbolic of love and devotion. Emeralds are even believed to change colour upon infidelity!

Emeralds have long been thought to possess healing powers. While today we know that Emeralds are not a cure for all medical and psychological problems, many people still use Emeralds to sooth their eyes and bring them good health. In fact, green has long been considered a soothing colour and it is no coincidence that the "green room" in theatres and TV studios is supposed to relax a performer after the stress and eyestrain of studio and stage lights.

A truly ancient gemstone, there is archeological evidence that the Babylonians may have been marketing Emeralds as early as 4,000 B.C.

The history of Egyptian Emeralds dates back over 4,000 years. Located in Egypt's eastern desert region, ancient miners braved extreme heat, scorpions and snakes to search for the

A traditional design containing 7 large oval cut Emeralds

A glamourous piece containing a central Emerald flanked by 6 Diamonds

4 Perfectly matched Emeralds set into a modern style white gold ring

A mixture of Emerald, Ruby, Alexandrite and Diamond, each gem as dazzling as the next

EMERALD

"Green Fire". Interestingly, Greek miners once laboured there for Alexander the Great.

The ancient mines of Egypt were rediscovered in 1818 by the French explorer Caillaud. Finding the mine with the help of the Egyptian government, he noted that Emeralds were probably worked there long after the Kings and Queens of Egypt ruled the land.

The Egyptians were known to engrave Emeralds with the symbol for foliage to represent eternal youth, burying these jewels with their dead.

Emeralds were said to be the favourite gem of Cleopatra. She often wore lavish Emerald jewellery, and bestowed visiting dignitaries with large Emeralds carved with her likeness when they departed Egypt.

Egyptian Emeralds were first mined some 2,000 years before Cleopatra's birth. During her reign, Cleopatra claimed these Emerald mines as her own, as well as the world's oldest source of Peridot, the fog-wrapped, desert isle of Zeberget (St. John's Island). Zeberget Peridot has a uniquely Emerald-like colour, due to its high nickel content. This is probably why many of Cleopatra's "Emeralds" were later found to be Peridots.

The ancient Romans associated Emeralds with fertility and rebirth, dedicating it to Venus, their goddess of love and beauty. The Roman historian, Pliny the Elder, once said of Emeralds "Nothing green is greener" and recorded that the Roman Emperor Nero, while presiding over gladiatorial fights, wore spectacles made of Emeralds.

The legends and lore surrounding Emeralds would not be complete without recounting the infamous stories of the Conquistador Hernando Cortés, who started his campaign against the Aztecs in 1519, and Francisco Pizarro, who commenced his military operation against the Incas in 1526.

When Hernando Cortés planted the Spanish flag on Aztec soil, he snatched from the berated Emperor Montezuma an enormous pyramid shaped Emerald, so big it could be seen from 100 yards away!

This eye catching blend of green and red is a great example of Emerald's versatility

Another popular choice with males and females alike

A stunning Zambian Emerald set regally in a white gold setting surrounded by 20 African Diamonds

The unusual green hue on this gem is greatly accentuated by the traditional yellow gold setting

EMERALD

This fine, delicate ring contains a unique cross prong selling

The traditional cross design is given an enchanting makeover

A captivating Columbian Emerald bracelet

Just the facts

The neon green colour of Emerald is unparalleled in the gem kingdom. Its beautiful green colour, combined with its rarity, makes Emerald one of the world's most valuable gemstones.

Emeralds are a member of the Beryl family of minerals. Minute traces of chromium, vanadium and iron give Emeralds their famous "Green Fire". The green crystals grow slowly within metamorphic rocks and are restricted in size by the host rock, making large Emeralds rare and costly. But did you know that large Emeralds are much more common than large Sapphires or Rubies?

Unlike other Beryls, Emeralds normally contain inclusions and tiny fractures. These are commonly called "Jardin", from the French word for "Garden", because of their resemblance to foliage. For Emeralds, Jardin is not looked on as a negative aspect as it would be for some other gem varieties, but instead is considered part of the Emerald's character and can be used to assure the purchaser of a natural gemstone.

Although Emeralds are relatively hard and durable, they must be protected from harsh blows because the Jardin found within makes them susceptible to breaking.

The famous "Emerald Cut" was developed specifically for this gem to reduce the amount of pressure exerted during cutting.

Emeralds are faceted in gem cuts for jewellery, whilst translucent material is cut and polished into cabochons and beads. Trapiche Emeralds are also cut into cabochons, making exquisite jewellery pieces.

A very small number of Emeralds display asterism and chatoyancy; these too are cut into cabochons.

When buying Emeralds, the most important consideration is always colour, with clarity and quality of cut playing second fiddle. Nevertheless, the brightness of the gemstone

EMERALD

(which is somewhat determined by the cutting and clarity) is also an important factor.

Traditionally, deep green is the most desired colour in Emeralds. Paler Emeralds are sometimes called "Green Beryl".

Although throughout this guide, we have generally not broken down the different features of gems from different locations, we felt that the Emerald was worthy of geographical analysis.

Colombian Emerald

Known for their vivid green colour, Colombian Emeralds are usually of exceptional quality. Colombia is, by tradition and lore, the finest modern source for Emeralds. With each comprised of many individual mines, there are three main areas of Emerald mining in Colombia; Muzo, Coscuez and Chivor.

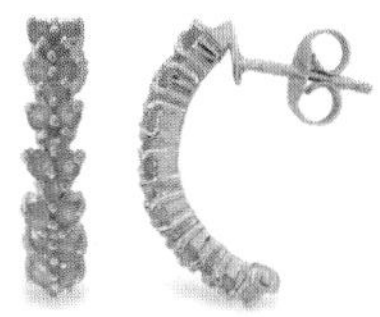

Over 40 expertly hand cut Emeralds make up these truly dramatic earrings

Muzo Colombian Emerald

The famed Muzo mines lie 100 miles North of Bogota. Emerald crystals from Muzo tend to have more saturated colour than either Coscuez or Chivor. They are considered the finest Emerald mines in the world.

The central diamond shape is made up of 9 colour matched Emeralds

A rare, prized form of Emerald, found only in the Muzo mining district of Colombia, Trapiche Emeralds are extremely unusual. Star-shaped rays that emanate from their centre in a hexagonal pattern characterise these Emeralds. These rays appear much like asterism but, unlike asterism, they are not caused by light reflection from tiny parallel inclusions, but by black carbon impurities that happen to form in the same pattern.

A magnificent 5.1ct Emerald forms the centre piece of this dazzling design

Coscuez Colombian Emerald

The Emerald crystals of Coscuez tend to exhibit a very wide range of colours but, unfortunately, also tend to be more included than those from Muzo. While Muzo and Coscuez are Colombia's most prolific Emerald producing

A huge Emerald necklace fit for kings and queens

EMERALD

locales, with the majority of Emeralds seen on the world market coming from these two areas, today Coscuez produces approximately sixty percent of Colombia's "Green Fire".

Chivor Colombian Emerald

Chivor Emeralds are best known for their bluish caste and generally have fewer inclusions and a lighter colour than either Coscuez or Muzo Emeralds. The Chivor mining area is the smallest area of the three and is separate from Muzo and Coscuez, which lay adjacent to each other.

The distinctive setting gives this pendant a regal feel

Brazilian Emerald

While Colombian Emeralds are known for their vivid green colour, Brazilian Emeralds are known for their variety of colour, ranging from light green to fine to medium dark blue green.

Emeralds were first discovered in Brazil about 500 years ago, after the arrival of the Portuguese. However, it was only in 1963 that the first samples with commercial value were found in Bahia, close to the town of Paraiso du Norte in Northern Brazil, effectively wiping out the notion that Brazil had no real "Green Fire" of its own.

4 round cut Emeralds encircle a central Yellow Sapphire

Zambian Emerald

Zambian Emeralds are of high quality but not as neon green as Colombian Emeralds, occasionally showing a slight yellowness in colour.

Although Zambia has the world's second largest Emerald deposit, this is substantially underdeveloped and restricted to approximately 40 artisanal mines near Kagem, Kitwe, Miku and Mufulira in Northern Zambia.

The stunning result of Emerald paired with white gold and Ruby

Pakistani Emerald

While an extremely harsh climate prevents the mining of Emerald deposits at higher altitudes, at lower elevations in the Swat Valley lie the

A kaleidoscope of colour with an Emerald taking centre stage

EMERALD

Gujar Kili mine and the ancient and historically significant Mingora mine.

Only a footpath beside the Kotkai River, winding its way through the narrow rugged valley, leads to the spectacular setting for the Gujar Kili mine. Severe weather conditions restrict operations during winter, making the hand-dug output very limited.

The Pakistani government tightly controls the mining of Emeralds from relatively new deposits discovered in 1960 in the Himalayan Mountains.

Siberian Emerald

Siberian Emerald, is long prized for its breathtaking clarity, green fire and forest hues.

According to history, Siberian Emerald was discovered by a Russian peasant in 1831, in the roots of a tree that had been felled in a storm on the Tokovoya River near Ekaterinburg in Siberia's Ural Mountains. Despite this, rumours persist that Russia actually supplied Emeralds long before the discovery of Colombian Emeralds. These legends even go as far as to suggest that the Scythian Emeralds, mentioned by Pliny the Elder in his Historia Naturalis, came from the Urals.

Rising to fame in the 19th Century, the largest and best known Siberian Emerald mine is the Mariinsky (St. Mary's). This mine was discovered in 1833 near the village of Malyshevo. The deposits were nationalised after World War I and Emerald mining soon ceased when Malyshevo became a military security zone. Siberian Emeralds then almost entirely disappeared...

Thanks to Don "The Gem Hunter", Siberian Emerald is now back and we are delighted to offer an amazing selection exclusively to Gems TV customers! Distinguished by a delicate green fire and a beautiful clarity, Siberian Emeralds are a "must have" for any true Emerald connoisseur. Feel like an empress with Siberian Emerald in a gorgeous array of handcrafted 18k and 9k gold jewellery.

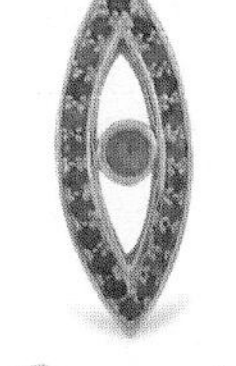

A breath-taking design that draws inspiration from influences from all over the world

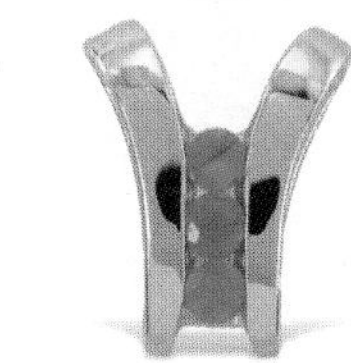

The bar setting of this pendant holds these gems perfectly in place

EMERALD:	May's birthstone
Locations:	Zambia, Zimbabwe, Brazil, Colombia, Pakistan
Colours Found:	Neon green
Typical Cuts:	Emerald, octagon, round, oval, cushion
Family:	Beryl
Hardness:	7.00 - 8.00
Refractive Index:	1.57 - 1.58
Relative Density:	2.67 - 2.78

FLUORITE

Deriving its name from the Latin word "Fluere", meaning to flow (reference to its low melting point and use in metal smelting), Fluorite is known as "the world's most colourful gemstone".

Fluorite, from which we get the word "fluorescent", crosses an entire spectrum of colour, from deep purple to crimson red, paraiba blue to emerald green (i.e. Chrome Fluorite) and frosty orange to lemon yellow. Fluorite is one of the more famous fluorescent minerals. Many specimens strongly fluoresce, in a great variation of colour.

An impressive 18.7ct Colour Change Fluorite makes up this regal looking pendant

This Brazilian Fluorite gives a perfect example of the gem's multi-colour banding

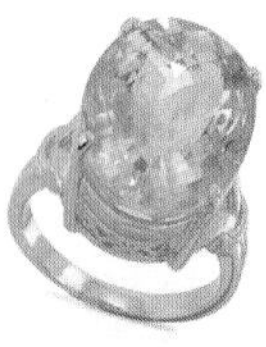

An example of an oval cut being used to show the glassy lustre often found in Fluorite

FLUORITE:	Bi-colour & multi-colour banding
Locations:	Brazil, India, Canada, China, England, Germany, Italy, Mexico, Norway, Russia, Switzerland, U.S.A
Colours Found:	Deep purple
Typical Cuts:	Baguette, oval
Family:	Fluorite
Hardness:	4.00
Refractive Index:	1.43
Relative Density:	3.20

Legends and lore

According to crystal healers, Fluorite is a third-eye gem bringing rationality to intuitive qualities. It is also believed to offer a stabilising energy, facilitating order, balance and healing. Fluorite is excellent for clarity of mind, objectivity, concentration and meditation.

Just the facts

A really eye-catching phenomenon of Fluorite is its distinctive bi-colour and multi-colour banding. Chunky Fluorite necklace strands optimise this exceptional effect. Interestingly, the "Blue John" variety mined in England, which possesses curved bands of blue purple, violet, yellow and white was used as an ornamental stone as far back as Roman times.

Colour Change Fluorite is mined in Bihar, India and shows a dramatic change from green to purple. Colour change gems are those that distinctly change their colour when viewed under two different light sources.

Due to its glassy lustre, Fluorite is highly sought after. Fluorite is the natural crystalline form of calcium fluoride (CaF2). It is a transparent to translucent, glassy mineral. When pure, fluorite is colourless; however, it usually contains impurities that colour it. The most common colours are violet, blue, green, yellow, brown, pink, and blue-black; a single crystal may have bands of several colours. Fluorite often forms beautiful cube-shaped crystals.

GARNET

Garnet has a history spanning more than 5,000 years. Having its root in the Latin word for seed, "Granatus" Garnet was so named because of its similar colour to pomegranate seeds.

From the svelte necklines of Abyssinian princesses to the powdered décolletages of Marie Antoinette, the captivating mystique of Garnets has made them a timeless symbol of feminine beauty. The imaginative lure of this "Queen of Gems" intoxicates the senses.

Unlike many other gemstones, colour in Garnet does not come from chemical impurities. When "Pure" a Garnet still has colour.

Legends and lore

Garnet's associated symbolism with pomegranates has been longstanding. Interestingly, several ancient pieces of jewellery have been unearthed that are studded with tiny red Garnets in cluster-like patterns reminiscent of pomegranates. The pomegranate is associated with eternity in Greek mythology and mentioned specifically in the legend of Hades' abduction of Persephone.

Garnet has long been associated with fire and was thought to possess the ability to illuminate the sky at night. Today, Garnets remain a symbol of faith, truth and light.

This story from Grimm's fairytales nicely presents the association - "Once upon a time an elderly lady came upon an injured bird. Taking the bird home with her, she nursed it back to health until one day it flew away. Although the lady thought she'd never see it again, it returned to her house with a Garnet that she put by her bedside. To her surprise, she awoke every night to see it shinning as bright as a torch, illuminating the bird's gratitude for her kindness."

According to biblical texts, during the Great Flood a radiant Garnet guided the way for Noah, ultimately leading his ark to salvation.

For Muslims, Garnets illuminate the fourth heaven.

A noble looking trilogy ring containing 3 stunning Mozambique Garnet gems

Two types of Garnet paired together to create this breathtaking design

14k gold and 11 Garnet gems result in this distinguished piece of jewellery

Flawlessly hand faceted this Mozambique Garnet shines with natural beauty

GARNET

Garnet jewellery was buried with Norsemen to light their passage to Valhalla and was also used to light the palace of Abyssinia's monarch.

The Crusaders set Garnets into their armour, believing their power would lead them to safety. During the Middle Ages Garnet was also believed to draw out negativity, ward off harm and increase well-being, chivalry, loyalty and honesty.

To receive a Garnet as a gift in the Middle Ages was considered good luck, however, if ever stolen, bad luck to the thief! It was also believed that a Garnet's loss of lustre was a sign of impending doom.

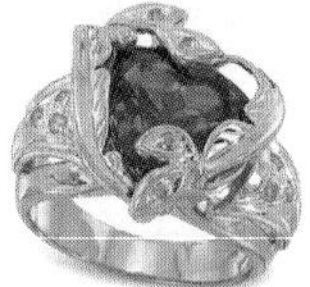

The yellow hues of this colour change Garnet are dramatically enhanced by the surrounding Yellow Diamonds

Although Garnet was the "fashion gem" of the 18th and 19th Centuries, the inadequacy of available chemical tests often resulted in it being confused with dark Ruby.

Jewellery set with Garnets from Czechoslovakia was particularly admired and, although today the Garnets are mined elsewhere, Bohemian style Garnet jewellery has retained its popularity.

This exotic design is a blend of Tsavorite, Garnet, Tanzanite and Yellow Diamond

In 1912, Garnets were made the official birthstone for January by the American National Association of Jewellers. It is also the gemstone for Aquarians and a traditional gift for 2nd and 6th wedding anniversaries.

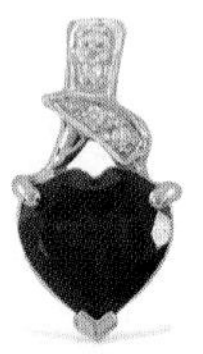

A 2ct Mozambique Garnet delicately shaped as a heart and flanked by Diamonds

Just the facts

Even though there are 29 different types of Garnets, appearing in as many colours, when you say "Garnet" most people automatically think of small dark red gemstones.

In fact, Garnets offer enough variety for every taste and can consequently keep up with the fast pace of changes in fashion!

A striking design containing highly desired Demantoid Garnet

Over the next six pages there are detailed descriptions of our top ten favourite Garnets. For more information on Garnets please visit our website: www.GemsTV.com

Colour Change Garnet

Colour Change Garnets are one of the rarest, most interesting and phenomenal of all gemstones. An extremely rare variety of Malaia Garnet, Colour Change Garnets are in fact a mixture of Pyrope, Almandine and Spessartite Garnet.

The colour change can be intense and equal to the colour change of top quality Alexandrite. As a result, Colour Change Garnets can easily be mistaken for Alexandrite.

Some of the best Colour Change Garnets are mined from a deposit in Bekily, Southern Madagascar. Colour Change Garnets from this mine are well known for their strong Alexandrite-like colour change.

Demantoid Garnet

Demantoid Garnet is one of the most desirable of all coloured gemstones and extremely rare. Discovered in 1855 in the Russian Central Ural Mountains, at two alluvial deposits, it was first assumed to be Emerald and even took the name "Uralian Emerald" until gemologists took a closer look.

The name Demantoid originates from the old German word "Demant" meaning "Diamond Like", because of a lustre and dispersion that yields a fire even higher than Diamonds! Interestingly, the famous Russian goldsmith Karl Fabergé liked to use Demantoid Garnets in his jewellery.

Commonly known as "Horsetail" inclusions, some Demantoid Garnets have golden byssolite strands that form beautiful patterns similar to the tail of a horse. Demantoids with prominent horsetail inclusions are particularly valued.

Small-scale mining recommenced in Russia in 1991. Today, most Demantoid Garnets are sourced from relatively new deposits beneath the scorched desert sands of Namibia.

Due to the fact that it has a fire greater than that of Diamonds, Demantoid Garnet is an absolute "must have" for any serious collector.

GARNET

Demantoid Garnet

This impressive piece contains 28 Sapphires and 76 Diamonds as well as a rare Colour Change Garnet

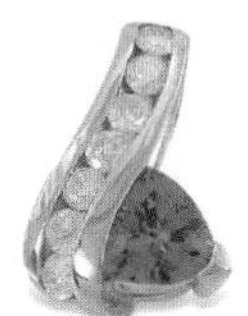

Modern elegance created by channel set Diamonds and flawless trilliant cut Demantoid Garnet

Simple yet chic Demantoid Garnet 9k gold earrings

GARNET

Hessonite Garnet

A perfect blend of Tanzanian Hessonite Garnet and Madagascan Tourmaline

Hessonite Garnet in a simple, elegant 9k gold ring

The natural lustre of the gem shows why it is so often called the 'Cinnamon Stone'

The inner brilliance of Malaia Garnet is obvious in this rich red gem

Hessonite Garnet

Hessonites come in two colours, golden and cinnamon (this variety is commonly known as the "Cinnamon Stone"). A perfectly coloured Hessonite is a bright golden-orange that resembles a combination of honey and orange with an internal fire. Some Hessonites have tints of red and brown.

Popular for thousands of years, the ancient Greeks and Romans used it in jewellery, cameos and intaglio (i.e. a figure cut into a gem so as to make the design depressed below the surface; whereas in a cameo the relief is risen above the surface). Interestingly, its name comes from the Greek word "Esson", meaning "Inferior", because it is softer than other Garnet varieties.

Widely used in Vedic astrology, Hessonite is known as "Gomedha" in Hindi. The ancient Hindus believed that Hessonite was formed from the fingernails of the great demon Vala, which were scattered in the lakes of the East. Vedic astrologists believe that, when set in gold, Hessonite is a powerful talisman that increases your lifespan and happiness.

Hessonite is common in the gem gravels of Sri Lanka and practically all Hessonite is obtained from this locality, although it is also found in Africa.

While the clearest gems are most prized, inclusions in Hessonite are common, with unique treacle-like streaks giving Hessonite an oily or even glasslike appearance.

Malaia Garnet

Discovered in the mid 1960's in Tanzania's Umba Valley, this red-orange to pink-orange variety of Garnet was originally thought to be Spessartite Garnet.

Actually a mixture of Pyrope, Almandine and Spessartite, Malaia Garnets are lively gems that exhibit sparkling red flashes. Once discovered not to be Spessartite, it aptly became known by the Swahili word "Malaia" meaning "Outcast".

Malaia Garnets are available in numerous shades of orange, ranging from soft peach to intense reddish orange.

Mandarin & Spessartite Garnet

Mandarin Garnets are the intensely bright orange red varieties of the rare orange Spessartite Garnet, also known as Spessartine.

Spessartite Garnet is named after its first discovery in Spessart, Bavaria in the mid-eighteen hundreds. Spessartite Garnet, once an extremely rare gem, is now enjoying a newfound popularity.

In 1991, Mandarin Garnets were discovered embedded in mica in northwest Namibia where the Kunene River borders Namibia and Angola. In 1994, new deposits were unearthed in southwest Nigeria. Soon after, Tanzania, the powerhouse of African gems, yielded deposits at the fabled gemstone mines of Arusha and Lelatema.

Although initially called "Kunene Spessartine" or "Hollandine", the evocative name "Mandarin Garnet" was soon adopted.

Mozambique Garnet

Originating in the East African nation they are named after, Mozambique Garnets are famed for their high quality and wonderfully warm, red colours.

Mozambique Garnet is a mixture of Pyrope and Almandine Garnet, similar in colour to Rhodolite Garnet, but slightly redder and darker.

Pyrope Garnet

Hear the word "Garnet", and what invariably comes to mind is the image of the deep red Pyrope Garnets belonging to the Pyralspites family. Pyrope comes from the Greek word "Pyropos", meaning "Fiery Eyed".

Fine Pyrope Garnets may be visually confused with dark Rubies. It was the "Fashion Gem" of the 18th and 19th Centuries and many "Rubies"

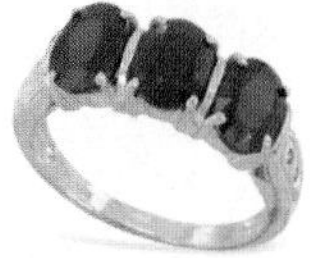

Flawlessly hand cut Mandarin Garnet

An eyecatching design containing Spessartite Garnet bordered by Sapphires and Aquamarines

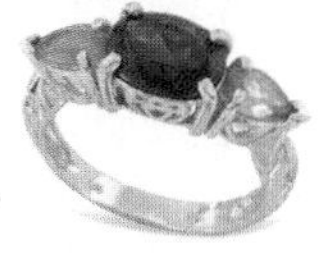

Superbly faceted Mozambique Garnet flanked by Alexandrite

Nick Davies
Gems TV Presenter

"All items of jewellery shown in this guide were crafted by Gems TV during 2005 and were sold direct to the public. The average selling price was amazingly under £65!

During 2006 we anticipate introducing a further 22,700 individual designs, featuring approximately 490 different gem types."

GARNET

Rhodolite Garnet

A splendid pairing of Rhodolite Garnet and Pink Tourmaline

A total of 12 Rhodolite Garnet gems make up these feminine earrings

Rhodolite Garnet gems displaying purple hues and set into white gold

The rare purple hues of Rhodolite Garnet are brilliantly drawn out in this piece by pairing it with Tanzanite

of this period were later found to be Pyrope Garnets.

Rhodolite Garnet

The name "Rhodolite" is taken from the Greek "Rho'Don" and "Lithos", which literally translates to "Rose Stone". Possessing a colour reminiscent of the rhododendron flower, this name was first used in the late 19th Century to describe Garnets discovered in North Carolina, U.S.A.

Unusually striking, Rhodolites are a naturally occurring blend of Almandine and Pyrope Garnet. While raspberry is the most prized colour, Rhodolites are also found in shades of pink through lavender.

Rhodolites are typically found as water-worn pebbles in alluvial deposits but are occasionally found in volcanic rock. The most spectacular Rhodolites are mined in Sri Lanka, Zimbabwe and from a relatively new deposit in the Kangala area of Tanzania that was discovered in 1987.

Due to its bright transparent clarity, Rhodolite is often cut into fantasy shapes.

Tough, durable, never enhanced and easily cleaned, Rhodilites are ideal for jewellery.

Colour is the most important characteristic when evaluating Rhodilites. The colour must be intense and uniform with a tone that is not too light or too dark. Rhodilites should be eye clean with minimal inclusions under magnification.

Star Garnet

A highly unusual form of Garnet is the rare four-rayed Almandine Star Garnet. While Almandine Garnets (also known as "Almandite") are the most common variety of Garnets, those displaying the star are not at all common. Available in deep reds, Almandine Star Garnets are found in Nigeria and Tanzania.

Asterism, or the star effect, is a reflection effect that appears as two or more intersecting bands of light across the surface of a gem.

Tsavorite Garnet

For some the '60s swung, for gemologists they rocked. The decade which had most people looking to the sky for Lucy's Diamonds had gemologists transfixed by a myriad of precious gemstones hailing from Africa's arid savannas: Fancy Sapphires, Rubies, Tourmaline, Tanzanite and a plethora of gorgeous coloured Garnets, amongst them a brilliant green Grossular-Garnet - Tsavorite. Tsavorite, East Africa's beautiful green gemstone is rightful heir to the title "The King of Garnets".

Some 37 years after its discovery, Tsavorite has comfortably established itself as one of the world's most beautiful, precious and desirable gemstones.

Tsavorite Garnet, comparable in scarcity to Demantoid Garnet, is extremely rare. In fact, it is so rare that it might be unavailable in future years.

Tsavorite's beautiful green hues are similar to the very best Emeralds. Tsavorite's brilliant green colours have overcome its lack of romantic lore and ancient history.

First discovered in 1967 by the now legendary Scottish geologist, Campbell R. Bridges, Tsavorite has quickly found favour as a precious coloured gem of choice. Bridges first discovered Tsavorite in Tanzania, but, in those days, getting an export license to take the gems out was impossible. In 1971, Bridges discovered Tsavorite for a second time in Kenya's Tsavo region.

Life in Africa's bush is dangerous and the Tsavo region is well known as the domain of man-eating lions and poachers, so, in order to protect himself from predators and brigands, Bridges was forced to live in a tree house. And, as he didn't want his treasure to be stolen, he cunningly used the local's fear of snakes by placing a python in amongst the Tsavorite rough.

Tsavorite eventually found its way to America where Henry Platt of Tiffany & Co. named the gemstone, basing its name on the famous Tsavo

Tsavorite Garnet

Beautifully cut, these Tsavorite Garnets display perfect brilliance

A contemporary twist on the traditional heart design

An 18k white gold design perfectly finished with 3 African Tsavorite gems

GARNET

National Park in Kenya.

Tsavorite took the world by storm and interest increased dramatically when, in 1974, Tiffany's started a special campaign promoting Tsavorite, making it well known in the U.S.A. International promotional campaigns followed and soon the global demand for Tsavorite reached epic proportions.

At one time, Tsavorite was being mined from 40 different areas throughout Tanzania and Kenya, of these, only four mining ventures are still producing commercial quantities. While some 50 deposits have been found in Kenya, Tanzania, Madagascar and even Zambia, only a handful of small mines produce commercially viable quantities.

GARNET:	January's birthstone
Locations:	Tanzania, Madagascar, Namibia, Russia, Sri Lanka, Mali, Nigeria, Mozambique, Kenya, Zimbabwe
Colours Found:	Bright orange red, red-orange to pink-orange, dark red, golden, cinnamon, pink through lavender, brilliant green, light pinkish-purple
Typical Cuts:	All cuts, beads
Family:	Garnet
Hardness:	7.25
Refractive Index:	1.70 - 1.73
Relative Density:	3.51 - 3.65

Lynn Garnett
Gems TV Presenter

"All items of jewellery shown in this guide were crafted by Gems TV during 2005 and were sold direct to the public. The average selling price was amazingly under £65!

During 2006 we anticipate introducing a further 22,700 individual designs, featuring approximately 490 different gem types."

HELIODOR

Heliodor was first discovered in Rossing, Erongo in Western Namibia in 1910 and was named from the Greek "Helios" and "Doron", meaning "gift from the sun".

Appearing in yellow, yellow-green, orange, and brown colours, Heliodor is the yellow variety of Beryl, the "Mother of Gemstones".

Interestingly, pure Beryl is colourless, with traces of different impurities being responsible for this gemstone's great colour range.

Just the facts

Heliodor is famous for its perfect, six-sided prismatic hexagon crystals that usually occur individually. These are often enormous and some 30 foot (8 metre), well-crystallised examples are known to have existed (of course very little of this was of a sufficient grade to be faceted).

With a hardness of 7.5 - 8, Heliodor is well suited to jewellery.

Heliodor can be faceted into various gem cuts, and some gems display chatoyancy (cat's eye effect) when cut and polished into cabochons.

Heliodor does not include golden colours that are aptly given the name of Golden Beryl. To see a list of the Beryl family turn to page 23.

The golden colour is produced when iron replaces some of the aluminium in the crystal structure.

Heliodor was discovered in a location that also produced Aquamarine (which is also coloured by iron).

The largest faceted Heliodor weighs in at a massive 2,054ct and is on display at the Smithsonian Institution in Washington D.C.

Heliodor is found in Minas Gerais and Goias, Brazil; the Ukraine in Russia; and also in Connecticut and Maine.

Heliodor can be faceted into various cuts, and some gems display the cat's eye effect when cut and polished into cabochons.

When perfect, transparent, six-sided crystals are discovered, they are sometimes set uncut in necklaces and pendants.

A delicate heart shape gem bezel set in 9k gold to produce this elegant ring

Brazilian Heliodor teamed with Diamonds makes this delightful children's pendant

HELIODOR:	Perfect, 6-sided prismatic hexagon crystals
Locations:	Madagascar, Brazil, Russia, Namibia, Nigeria, U.S.A, Russia, Tajikistan
Colours Found:	Yellow, yellow-green, orange, brown
Typical Cuts:	All cuts
Family:	Beryl
Hardness:	7.50 - 8.00
Refractive Index:	1.57 - 1.60
Relative Density:	2.80

HERDERITE

A very unusual cut for a very rare gemstone

18k gold, beautiful shoulder Diamonds and Herderite - simply stunning

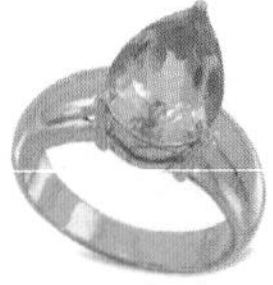
The pear shape cut of this Herderite highlights its natural lustre

A rare 8.9ct of Herderite went into making this stunning 18k gold pendant

An unusual design made more distinctive with the use of an antique cut Herderite gem

HERDERITE:	Thermoluminescent
Locations:	Brazil, Germany, Russia, U.S.A, Madagascar
Colours Found:	Colourless, white, yellow, green or light blue
Typical Cuts:	Pear
Family:	Herderite
Hardness:	5.00 - 5.50
Refractive Index:	1.59 - 1.62
Relative Density:	2.90 - 3.00

Herderite is an attractive yet very rare mineral. It was named for Siegmund August Wolfgang Von Herder (1776-1838), mining official in Freiberg, Saxony, Germany, where it was first discovered.

Just the facts

Its twinned crystals (i.e. one crystal growing within another) are one of its most noteworthy forms.

One of Herderite's other characteristics is that it is thermoluminescent, meaning it may glow with a weak blue light upon extreme heating. It is also sometimes fluorescent, showing deep blue in long wave ultraviolet light. It can be colourless, white, yellow, green or light blue.

The gem is mined in Minas Gerais, Brazil, Germany and Russia. In the U.S.A, there are several locations that mine the gem such as Newery, Maine, New Hampshire and San Diego, however, the percentage of rough that makes its way into jewellery is extremely minimal.

Herderite has a vitreous lustre and a very complicated crystal structure.

Our Herderite jewellery

Don't expect to find a lot of Herderite in this year's collection. Throughout 2005, we were only able to source two pieces of the gem. Whenever we do discover it, as it is so rare, we will always set it in 18k gold.

Don Kogen, the Gem Hunter says:

"Our buyers are constantly travelling the globe hunting gems. On our travels, we occasionally come across a small quantity of gems that we weren't expecting to find. When this happens, regardless of the economics involved, we will always try and obtain them in order to offer the widest selection of gems to our customers and collectors. Herderite was such a find. We have included it in this guide in the hope that we will soon discover more of this beautiful gem."

HIDDENITE

Hiddenite is an attractive and rare gemstone. It has an unusual green colour that is unlike either Peridot or Emerald. Hiddenite was discovered in 1800 in Hiddenite, a city in Alexander County, North Carolina. Both the city and the gem mineral were named after William Earl Hidden, a mineralogist and mining director from Newark, New Jersey who was mining in the area.

Just the facts

Hiddenite is actually one of two varieties of Spodumene. The other is Kunzite, a pink to lilac variety. Kunzite is the more common of the two and is better known by most gemstone collectors.

The green colour of Hiddenite ranges from a yellowish to a bluish green. The gemstone is strongly pleochroic meaning that it can change colour when viewed from different angles, thus a gem cutter must take care to orient the stone in the best position for the deepest colour.

Hiddenite is formed from Lithium Aluminum Silicate (LiAlSi2O6). The crystals are vitreous and can be in either transparent or translucent form. For many years, occurrence of Hiddenite was limited to only North Carolina, however, new deposits were recently discovered in Madagascar and Brazil.

Hiddenite is used as both a collecting specimen and as a gemstone. Due to its strong pleochroism, Hiddenite requires skill and expertise to cut and facet. The top and bottom of the crystal reveal the deepest colours and knowledgeable gem cutters take advantage of this effect to produce the finest quality Hiddenite.

Typing Hiddenite into any Internet search engine will provide hundreds of results about the city of Hiddenite in North Carolina in the U.S.A. As you start to discover today's life style in this historical city, you can't help but become attached to this wonderful gem.

Because it's so scarce, if you fall in love with Hiddenite when you see it - Snatch It!

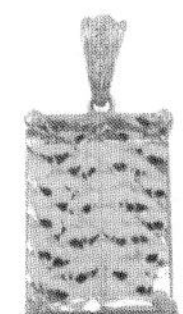

The dispersion of light through this Hiddenite gem is enhanced by our expert gem cutters

With Hiddenite at its centre this pendant is mysteriously captivating

Simple and elegant this pendant is timelessly beautiful

HIDDENITE:	Pleochroism
Locations:	U.S.A, Madagascar, Brazil
Colours Found:	Yellowish to a blue-ish green
Typical Cuts:	Fancy, princess, emerald, baguette, pear
Family:	Spodumene
Hardness:	6.50
Refractive Index:	1.65 - 1.68
Relative Density:	1.66

IDOCRASE

Legends and lore

Idocrase derives its name from the Greek language and means "Mixed Form", an allusion to its crystals showing a mixture of other mineral forms.

The word itself is derived from the Greek words "Eidos" (likeness) and "Krasis" (composition). Idocrase, also known as Vesuvianite, is a fascinating mineral found originally on the volcano, Mt. Vesuvius, hence one of the names.

Idocrase is both rare and beautiful and is extremely popular amongst mineral collectors.

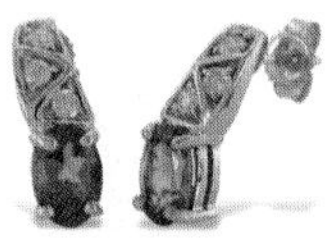

The unusual pave setting of Diamonds in these earrings draws the attention toward the Idocrase below

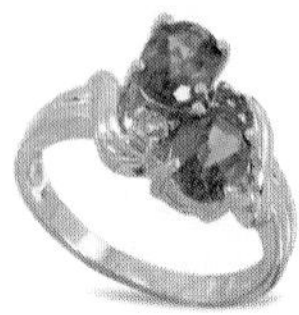

The gorgeous green colour of these Idocrase gems is beautifully highlighted by the Yellow Sapphires

IDOCRASE:	Vitreous to resinous lustre
Locations:	Canada, U.S.A, Italy, Russia, Switzerland
Colours Found:	Green, brown, yellow, blue, purple
Typical Cuts:	Emerald, octagon, round, oval, trilliant, cabochon
Family:	Idocrase
Hardness:	6.50
Refractive Index:	1.70
Relative Density:	3.30 - 3.50

Just the facts

The crystals show a square cross-section perpendicular to the long axis. Idocrase produces some very nicely shaped crystals.

Oddly enough, some of its crystal structure is similar to that of Grossularite, a Garnet, which is an isometric mineral. Idocrase forms as a result of contact between metamorphic rock and impure Limestone, and is usually found with other exotic minerals.

A massive green gem variety is called Californite, from where it is found.

Idocrase's colour is normally green, but also can be brown, yellow, blue and/or purple.

Idocrase occurs in Quebec, Canada; California and the New England region of U.S.A; Mt. Vesuvius, Italy; Russia and Switzerland.

Due to its green colour, Idocrase has often been confused for Jade. With a closer inspection, its crystal shape tends to reveal its true identity.

What our Craftsmen say:

Mr.Amnat Kaeowhom - Gem Setting

"If you love green jewellery and have already got Emeralds, Jade and Sapphire, then Idocrase will perfectly complement your existing collection. When the gem is in limited supply, we will often set them into rings and surround them by other complimentary green gems."

IOLITE

The name Iolite comes from the Greek word "Ios" which means violet. Iolite is a transparent, violet-blue, light blue or yellow-grey gemstone. A pleochroic gem, Iolite will show many colours in a single piece.

Legends and lore

Legend has it that the Vikings used thin pieces of Iolite as the world's first polarising filter. Looking through an Iolite lens, they could determine the exact position of the sun on overcast days and navigate their boats safely. Hence Iolite is also know as the "Viking's Compass".

Known as the gemstone of clear vision, when worn as an amulet, Iolite was believed to have the power to guide lost sailors to the brilliance of the sun in order to find their way home.

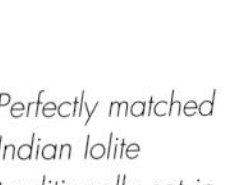

The simple prong setting of this pendant ensure the Iolite's full beauty is on show

Just the facts

Iolite is a popular and interesting gemstone. It has a gorgeous violet blue colour that is unlike other gemstones, although it has been compared to a light blue Sapphire. It is for this reason that it is sometimes known as "Water Sapphire".

Perfectly matched Indian Iolite traditionally set in 9k white gold

While we believe an Iolite necklace or Iolite earrings are probably the best ways to showcase this gem's unique colour, Iolite rings are also desirable, as it is a durable gem with a hardness of 7-7.5 on the Mohs scale.

This deep Purple Iolite gem is perfectly balanced by the lilac hues of surrounding Tanzanite

Pleochroism is very pronounced in Iolite and is seen as three different colour shades in the same gem. In viewing an Iolite, the colours violet blue, yellow grey and light blue can be seen. It is therefore very important to look at an Iolite from several directions before you purchase, because the gem will present very different colours from different angles. When cut properly, the gem will show its best blue colour through the top or table of the gem but, when viewed from another angle, the gem may appear colourless.

Most of the Iolite available today comes from Sri Lanka, India and Madagascar.

IOLITE:	Pleochroism
Locations:	Madagascar, Sri Lanka, India
Colours Found:	Violet-blue, light blue or yellow-grey
Typical Cuts:	All cuts
Family:	Cordierite
Hardness:	7.00 - 7.50
Refractive Index:	1.50
Relative Density:	2.53 - 2.65

JADE *(NEPHRITE)*

Nephrite Jade was known as the "Stone of Heaven" in ancient China. Nephrite Jade was excavated from the Kunlun Mountains of northwest China, from 5000 BC and, even today, China remains an important source for this gemstone.

Legends and lore

In Russia, Nephrite has been mined and crafted since 3000 BC. Tsar Alexander III's sarcophagus was carved from Nephrite. For about 3000 years, the gemstone has been highly prized by the Native North Americans of British Columbia, Canada, where it was known as "Greenstone".

Just the facts

For centuries, Nephrite Jade and the other Jade variety, Jadeite, were considered one and the same and it was not until 1863 that they were identified as different minerals with a similar appearance and properties.

Nephrite is composed of silica and magnesia and its colour is determined by the amount of iron present in the mineral. Less iron content produces lighter colours such as white, cream, yellow, grey, green, blue, red, brown and lavender. More iron content produces the darker coloured Nephrite, such as darker grey and darker green.

Nephrite has the highest tensile strength (i.e. toughness as opposed to hardness) of all natural gemstones and, in fact, has a tensile strength greater than some steel – it is so strong that it cannot be chiselled but has to be ground using sharp abrasives. In antiquity, it was often used in weaponry because of its great strength.

Interestingly, less than 0.05% of Nephrite extracted is of gem quality.

Jadeite

Jadeite is found in strongly metamorphosed sodium-rich serpentinous rocks, and is named from the Spanish "piedra de ijada" (stone of the side) as it was thought to cure kidney stones and other kidney ailments.

A modern piece of gentlemen's jewellery containing channel set Red Jade

The design of this pendant takes inspiration from Jade's traditional Chinese roots

A large Lavender Jade displaying the lustre that makes this gem so popular

JADE:	Highest tensile strength
Locations:	China, U.S.A, Mexico, Southern Zimbabwe, Australia, Canada
Colours Found:	White, cream, yellow, grey, green, blue,red, brown, lavender
Typical Cuts:	Cabochons, ornamentals
Family:	Jade and Nephrite
Hardness:	6.50
Refractive Index:	1.61 - 1.63
Relative Density:	2.90 - 3.10

JASPER

The name comes from the Latin name for the gem "Iaspis". Jasper is an opaque and fine-grained variety of Chalcedony. It is found in red, brown, pink, yellow, green, greyish white and shades of blue and purple.

Jasper is normally cut as cabochons and has traditionally been used as a gemstone for jewellery such as brooches, earrings, necklaces, pendants, intaglios (i.e. a design carved into or beneath the surface of a gemstone) and cameos.

Legends and lore

Jasper was a favourite gem in ancient times and is referenced in Greek, Hebrew, Assyrian and Latin literature. For example, Jasper is one of "The Stones of Fire" (Ezekiel 28:13-16) which were given to Moses at the Mountain of God and is said to possess the power to summon angels. Moses then decreed them mounted into a sacred breastplate for his brother, the high priest Aaron (Exodus 28:15-30). In the New Testament (Revelations 21:19), Jasper is one of the twelve gemstones set in the foundations of the city walls of Jerusalem. As compiled by Andreas, Bishop of Caesurae, one of the earliest writers to tie the Apostles with the symbolism of the twelve gems of Jerusalem, Jasper was for the Apostle St. Peter.

In some Native American cultures, Jasper is considered to be the symbolic blood of the Earth, and was thus thought to be one of the best gems for connecting with the deep, stabilising energies of the Earth.

According to crystal healers, Jasper is an intensely protective gem, acting to stabilise the aura and rid it of dysfunctional energy, thereby facilitating relaxation, contentment and compassion.

Just the facts

Jasper is a member of the Chalcedony family and is normally cabochon cut and set into rings, bracelets and pendants. Remember that no two pieces of Jasper will ever look the same.

The unique colouring of Jasper is eloquently highlighted when set in white gold

An elegant 9k gold pendant containing Mexican Grey Jasper

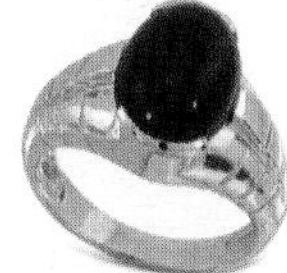

Bezel set Red Jasper in a sophisticated gentlemen's ring

JASPER:	Mentioned in the Bible
Locations:	India, Madagascar, Mexico, U.S.A, Germany, France, U.K
Colours Found:	Red, brown, pink, yellow, green, greyish white and shades of blue, purple
Typical Cuts:	Cabochons, beads, commesso
Family:	Chalcedony
Hardness:	6.50 - 7.00
Refractive Index:	1.54
Relative Density:	2.59 - 2.61

KORNERUPINE

Kornerupine was discovered in Fiskernaes, Greenland in 1884 and was named after the Danish geologist and explorer of Greenland, Andreas N. Kornerup (1857-1881). It is a rare gemstone well known for its pleochroism (i.e. different colours seen from different viewing angles) and its green colour, which often can be as intense as Emerald.

Legends and lore

Amongst crystal healers, Kornerupine is considered a gemstone for teaching and communication. Kornerupine is also said to help stabilise the emotional swings of manic-depressives and assists in seeing through the false agreements in one's current reality.

This double strand pendant contains 17 colour-matched Kornerupine gems

Just the facts

A metamorphic mineral, Kornerupine is a complex magnesium aluminium boro-silicate whose crystals are often found in gravel deposits collected behind rocks or in the bends of rivers. Kornerupine is often deposited with other gems including Sapphire, Chrysoberyl, Ruby, Topaz, Garnet, Zircon, Diopside, Andalusite, Spinel and Iolite.

A modern design pendant containing Madagascan Kornerupine

While Kornerupine has a similar, but slightly higher, index of refraction to Emeralds and similar characteristic inclusions, the two gems are easily distinguished by Kornerupine's pleochroism. Depending on the angle at which Kornerupine is viewed, its colours can range from brown, colourless, green, greenish-yellow, yellow, pink or lavender. However, wherever possible, Kornerupine is faceted on the green axis as this colouration is its rarest colour and claims the highest price.

Kornerupine also occasionally exhibits chatoyancy or the cat's eye effect. When polished as cabochons, Kornerupine displays a reflection effect that appears as a single bright band of light across its surface. This effect is caused by inclusions of fine, slender, parallel fibres in the gem.

KORNERUPINE:	Pleochroism
Locations:	Sri Lanka, Madagascar, Australia, Kenya, Greenland
Colours Found:	Green
Typical Cuts:	Cabochon, oval, baguette, fancy
Family:	Kornerupine
Hardness:	6.50 - 7.00
Refractive Index:	1.66 - 1.68
Relative Density:	3.28 - 3.35

KUNZITE

Kunzite, discovered in California in 1902, was named after Tiffany's chief gemologist, G.F. Kunz.

Kunz described this fairly robust pastel pink gemstone as having two distinct properties: "Phosphorescence" where Kunzite, in this respect similar to Diamonds, is observed to glow in a darkened room after it has been exposed to the sun's ultra-violet rays; and "Pleochroism", showing two different colours when viewed from different directions.

These phenomena are best seen in larger sized gems set into jewellery like pendants, drop and chandelier earrings and rings with open prong or bar settings that let light flow freely through them, accentuating Kunzite's fire to full effect.

Kunzite radiates pure Parisian chic, revealing delicate raspberry pinks, frosty lilacs, cool lavenders and hot fuchsia under the warm glow of incandescent light.

Its subtle colouring is perfectly complimented by "décolleté" eveningwear, dreamy candlelight and tender blushes, hence its name "the evening gemstone".

A one of a kind huge 114.8ct of Kunzite

Legends and lore

Aside from their obvious physical beauty, pink gemstones possess potent metaphysical properties.

Alternative healers use a multitude of pink gems in conjunction with the "heart chakra". The 4th of 7 energy points that run the course of the human body, the "heart chakra" is believed to carry the emotional sensibilities of love and compassion.

Some believe that, when the 4th chakra is blocked, we experience emotions such as anxiety, fear, anger and frustration. Healers use the properties of pink gems like Pink Tourmaline and Kunzite to free the "heart chakra" from this negative energy.

This alternative approach of enhancing the "power of pink" is a viewpoint shared and supported by traditional methods of medicine and psychology:

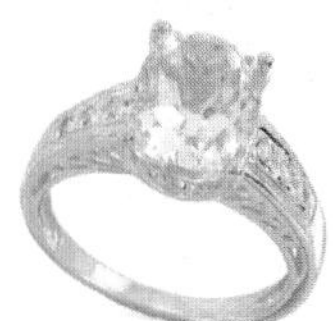

Precision faceting on this cushion cut Kunzite highlights this gem's inner fire

A glorious Kunzite surrounded by 60 points of Diamonds

This 9k white gold Kunzite ring featuring a modern double prong setting

KUNZITE

"The colour pink causes the brain to send signals that reduce the secretion of adrenaline, reducing the heart rate and consequently dissipating states of extreme excitement such as anger." *Science Digest, 1980*

Others believe that Kunzite is associated with gentleness, friendship, self-discipline, emotional balance, inner love, maturity, serenity, calmness, openness and moderation. Many also believe that Kunzite helps to attract gentle friends, thereby teaching us to combine compassion with discipline.

Just the facts

The lithium in Kunzite's chemical composition - LiAl (Si2O6), lithium aluminum silicate - gives it a wonderful pink-violet colour that compliments either autumn or spring wardrobes. It shows its colour well in larger sizes. In fact, the largest faceted Kunzite weighs a massive 880ct and is on display at the Smithsonian Institute in Washington D.C.

A massive 12.5ct Brazilian beauty

As a member of the Spodumene family, Kunzite is closely related to Hiddenite, the green variety of the mineral. Hiddenite is an attractive gem but is rare and for the most part is known only by collectors (see page 59).

A 4.5ct Kunzite, encircled by 16 Rhodolite Garnets

Kunzite is strongly pleochroic, meaning there is a colour intensity variation when a crystal is viewed from different directions. The top and the bottom of the crystal reveal the deepest colours and our experienced gem cutters take advantage of this when faceting Kunzite for Gems TV.

Kunzite is mined in Afghanistan, Brazil, Burma, Canada, Madagascar, Mexico, Pakistan, Russia, Sweden and the U.S.A.

KUNZITE:	Phosphorescence and pleochroism
Locations:	Afghanistan, Brazil, Pakistan, Madagascar, Canada, Mexico, Russia, Sweden U.S.A
Colours Found:	Pastel pink
Typical Cuts:	All cuts
Family:	Spodumene
Hardness:	6.00 - 7.00
Refractive Index:	1.65 - 1.68
Relative Density:	3.16 - 3.20

What our Craftsmen say:

Miss Amphorn Santamyae - Polishing

"A prelude to love, Pink is the colour of romance, seducing all who gaze into her opulent tones. Pink is the colour of passion, rousing and stimulating our innermost desires."

KYANITE

Also called Disthene, the name Kyanite is derived from the Greek "Kyanos", meaning "Blue". The most popular varieties display intense cornflower blues similar to Sapphire, and sparkling greenish-blues reminiscent of Aquamarine.

Legends and lore

The powerful blue hues of Kyanite have long been thought to inspire calmness, composure, serenity, loyalty and respect.

Kyanite is used by alternative healers as a tool for meditation and relaxation. These healers use Kyanite to open the third eye Chakra to enhance creativity, broaden perception and to reach a better understanding of others. Kyanite is also said to foster tranquillity, having a positive effect on dreams, visualisation and foresightedness.

1.1ct Kyanite, secured in a modern six prong setting and flanked by six Diamonds pave set into the shoulders

Just the facts

Kyanite is a rare Polymorph that displays two hardnesses within one gem. A unique characteristic among gem types, like Diamonds, Kyanite has perfect cleavage in one direction. This, combined with its varying hardness, makes Kyanite a challenging gem to cut - thus the quality of faceting for Kyanite is an important value consideration.

Two gorgeous Tibetan Kyanites brilliantly suspended in a bar setting

Occurring in a wide variety of locations around the world, the best quality Kyanite hails from the Kali Gandaki Region of West Central Nepal and Tibet.

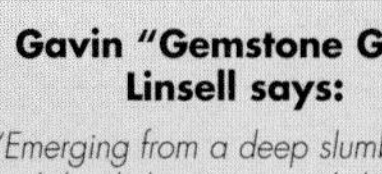

Gavin "Gemstone Gav" Linsell says:

"Emerging from a deep slumber, you push back the covers and slip out of bed, pondering what jewellery to wear. As you draw back the curtains on a revitalising summer's morning, your question is answered with the clear blue skies embodied in the atmospheric hues of cool blue Kyanite. Suitability is a key word when describing Kyanite, as it suits all skin tones and looks great set into yellow, white or rose gold jewellery."

KYANITE:	Perfect cleavage, varying hardness
Locations:	Nepal, Tibet
Colours Found:	Cornflower blues, sparkling greenish-blues
Typical Cuts:	Cabochon, emerald, octagon, oval
Family:	Kyanite
Hardness:	4.50 - 7.00
Refractive Index:	1.71 - 1.73
Relative Density:	3.56 - 3.68

LABRADORITE

Labradorite is named after the Labrador Peninsula in Canada where it was first discovered. Available in brilliant pastels and deep golden colours, Labradorite produces some stunning gem-quality stones perfect for wardrobes of all seasons.

Legends and lore

Calling it "Firestone" because of its captivating play of colour, the Native Indians of Labrador attributed mystical qualities to Labradorite, using the powdered gem as a magical potion to cure their ailments.

Interestingly, some modern mystics believe that Labradorite is a gem that assists the practice of magic, unleashes the power of the imagination and helps to overcome personal limitations.

Just the facts

Labradorite is a variety of Feldspar. Transparent Labradorite should be fine, clear and relatively free from inclusions, displaying shades that vary from an almost lime-yellow colour to bright canary yellows and golden tones.

Valued for its lustrous metallic reflections that are said to resemble a Brazilian butterfly's wing, this play of colour or "Schiller" is aptly called "Labradorescence" in gemological circles, and appears as stunning rainbow-coloured reflections when light strikes the gem in a particular direction.

Mainly caused by the interference of light from lattice distortions, this effect often appears in violet, blue, green, yellow and even orange-reddish tints.

When selecting dark smoke grey Labradorite, observe the strength and intensity of the "Labradorescence", when the gemstone is viewed from different angles. This may result in different colours being visible or even a range of colours all being visible at the same time.

A sodium-rich plagioclase Feldspar, Labradorite occurs in Canada, Australia, Madagascar, Russia, Mexico, China, the Scandinavian Peninsula and U.S.A.

Precision faceting at its best, this Brazilian Labradorite measured a massive 12mm x10mm

This pendant is a fine example of Labradorite's ability to demonstrate "Schiller"

Due to its play of colour, matching Labradorite is an especially challenging task for our craftsmen

LABRADORITE:	Lustrous metallic reflections
Locations:	Madagascar, China, India Canada, Australia, Russia, Mexico, the Scandinavian Peninsula, U.S.A
Colours Found:	Orange, yellow, colourless, red
Typical Cuts:	Flat surface cut, cabochon, fancy, cabochon, beads, ornamentals
Family:	Feldspar
Hardness:	6.00 - 6.50
Refractive Index:	1.55 - 1.57
Relative Density:	2.70 - 2.72

MALACHITE

Malachite is named after the Greek word "Moloche" for "Mallow", a green herb, due to its similarity in colour to mallow leaves.

A secondary copper mineral, Malachite is a popular gem that has light and dark vivid green banded areas. Many beautiful specimens of Malachite contain special combinations with other minerals, such as Azurite, Cuprite or Chrysocolla.

Legends and lore

In Rome, it was called the "Peacock Stone" and dedicated to the Goddess Juno, who protects against lightning and other perils of nature. Continuing these ancient traditions, to this day some Italians wear Malachite as protection from the evil eye.

According to legend, it was worn to detect impending danger and was assumed to break into pieces when danger was near. Hence, it was often regarded as the guardian gem of travellers.

According to modern crystal healers its powers include: protection, power, peace, hope, love, and success in business.

A modern gent's 3ct Cabochon Malachite ring

Demonstrating different shades of green, this Silver Malachite ring proved popular with younger customers

Just the facts

Malachite's banded light and dark green designs are unique and give it an ornamental quality unlike that of any other gem. The light and dark green bands are so distinctive that Malachite may be one of the minerals most easily recognised by the general public.

Although not a very rare gemstone, its ability to mix with other minerals has lead to Malachite being unearthed in a wide array of attractive colours and patterns. These unique combinations create some of the most intriguing results in the gem world. The following gems are all a form of Malachite; the Blue Azurite, sparkling Black Mottramite, the light Blue Chrysocolla and the rustic Red Limonite.

Because Malachite is a fairly soft gem, it is nearly always fashioned as a cabochon.

This Azurite Malachite from Arizona shows why the Romans called it the Peacock Stone

MALACHITE:	Banded light and dark green designs
Locations:	Zaire, Russia, Germany, Congo, Zambia, France, UK, Chile, Australia, Israel, Sweden, Mexico & U.S.A
Colours Found:	Banded light and dark green
Typical Cuts:	Cabochons, beads, ornamentals
Family:	Malachite
Hardness:	3.50 - 4.00
Refractive Index:	1.85
Relative Density:	3.90 - 4.00

MANGANOTANTALITE

At 11.45ct this Manganotantalite is especially rare and beautifully complimented with 25 points of pave set Diamonds

MANGANOTANTALITE:	Orthorhombic
Locations:	U.S.A, Brazil, Sweden, Pakistan
Colours Found:	Brownish-red
Typical Cuts:	Fancy, square, baguette, octagon
Family:	Tantalite
Hardness:	6.00 - 6.50
Refractive Index:	2.19 - 2.34
Relative Density:	8.10

Manganotantalite was first discovered in the town of Uto, Sweden in 1887, and named for its chemical composition, Manganiferous Tantalite.

Manganotantalite is extremely rare and is definitely one for the collectors.

Just the facts

Manganotantalite is a very rare collector's gem with a high dispersion and is the manganese-rich variety of Tantalite.

Manganotantalite is brownish-red in colour and is found in the U.S.A, Brazil, Sweden and Pakistan.

Manganotantalite exhibits brownish-black crystals with reddish internal reflections. It occurs in granite pegmatites and is commonly associated with Lepidolite.

MAWSITSIT

MAWSITSIT:	Fibrous texture, waxy to vitreous in lustre
Locations:	Burma
Colours Found:	Bright green rock, black inclusions
Typical Cuts:	Cabochons, ornamentals, carvings
Family:	Mawsitsit
Hardness:	6.00 - 8.00
Refractive Index:	1.52
Relative Density:	2.50 - 3.10

Mawsitsit was first identified by Swiss gemologist, Eduard Gubelin, in 1963. The famous gemologist was travelling in Burma and noticed a bright green rock with black inclusions being mined. It has taken over 30 years for this beautiful material to become available to the world at large.

A stone with a weird name, Mawsitsit is a high-chromium content cousin of Jadeite. It is found in only one deposit on Earth, in the village of the same name in northern Burma (Myanmar), where Imperial Jadeite is mined. It is famous for its vivid green tone with areas of black in the same specimen.

Mawsitsit is not considered Jade, but is similar in its look and toughness. Composed of Chrome Jadeite, Ureyite and Natrolite, it receives its lovely green colour from chromium and its black swirls from Ureyite.

MOONSTONE

Popular with the Romans, who thought it was formed out of moonlight, and in India, where it is considered a sacred zodiac stone, Moonstone is the most valuable variety of Feldspar and is becoming increasingly hard to find.

Legends and lore

A symbol of the Third Eye, Moonstone was once believed to balance yin/yang, protect against epilepsy and sun stroke, cure headaches and nose bleeds and ensure a high yield in crops. Today, crystal healers believe that it can help men open their feminine, emotional aspects.

In antiquity, during the full moon, men used Moonstone to predict the future, by placing them in their mouths!

A favourite of Art Nouveau jewellers, Moonstone is a highly prized gift for lovers as it is believed to arouse tender passion. In some cultures, it is also believed to accentuate the wearer's nature, whether positive or negative.

Moonstone pendant demonstrating beautiful chatoyancy

Nine perfectly matched Moonstones in a very modern setting

Just the facts

Moonstone is a member of the Feldspar group of minerals and is closely related to Sunstone. The name Feldspar comes from the German "Feldt Spat", meaning "Field Stone". This is because when Feldspar weathers, it releases large amounts of plant nutrients, such as potassium, which enrich the soil.

Moonstone's characteristic shimmer or sheen is also known as "Schiller" or "Aventurescence", and is caused by the intergrowth of two different types of Feldspar with different refractive indexes. Moonstones are usually cut in a smooth-domed cabochon shape to maximise this effect.

When Moonstone has a prefix, it is simply referring to its colour or visual effect. Some common examples include Cat's Eye Moonstone, Rainbow Moonstone and Star Moonstone.

MOONSTONE:	June's birthstone
Locations:	Madagascar, Tanzania, Sri Lanka, India, Brazil
Colours Found:	Colourless to grey, brown, yellow, green, rainbow, pink
Typical Cuts:	Cabochon
Family:	Feldspar
Hardness:	6.00 - 6.50
Refractive Index:	1.51 - 1.57
Relative Density:	2.56 - 2.62

MORGANITE

Morganite, or "Pink Beryl" as it was first termed, was discovered in Madagascar in 1911. It was Tiffany's celebrated gemologist, G.F. Kunz who renamed the unique pink gemstone in homage to the distinctive New York banker and his benefactor, John Pierport Morgan.

Legends and lore

While Morganite has had little time to generate myths and legend, aside from their obvious physical beauty, all pink gemstones possess potent metaphysical properties connected with love and compassion

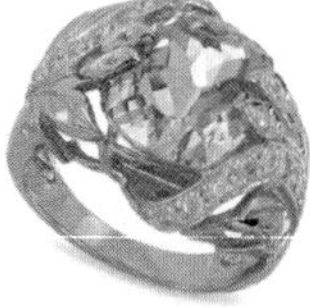

A 5.4ct Morganite from Brazil with 20 Mozambique White Topaz

Just the facts

Morganite is a member of the Beryl family and sister gem to Aquamarine and Emerald. It is coloured by trace amounts of manganese that find their way into the Beryl crystal structure. Morganite is found as flat, tabular crystals that resemble Rose Quartz, but Rose Quartz' lustre pales next to Morganite's fire.

A regal piece of Morganite with Diamonds set to the North, East, South and West

Today, Morganite is sourced from Madagascar, U.S.A and Brazil. Morganite, unlike its famous cousins originating from the same locales, possesses a hardness of 7.5 to 8.0 on the Moh's Scale.

Morganite comes in many fine shades of pink. Some are clearly bubblegum pink, whilst others tend more towards purple. Occasionally a slight orange hue may be seen.

MORGANITE:	Flat, tabular crystals
Locations:	Madagascar, Brazil, U.S.A
Colours Found:	Pink
Typical Cuts:	All cuts
Family:	Beryl
Hardness:	7.50 - 8.00
Refractive Index:	1.57 - 1.60
Relative Density:	2.71 - 2.90

Our Morganite jewellery

When Mother Nature created Morganite she made the ideal gemstone to complement all complexions. Coming in all shades from subtle lavenders to hot fuchsias Morganite exudes feminine charm and tenderness providing the perfect antidote to the stress of modern life.

The hardness, lustre and myriad of beautiful pink hues make Morganite immensely suitable as a jewellery gemstone for everyday wear. The only factor that impedes Morganite's popularity is its rarity.

MOTHER OF PEARL

While Queen Elizabeth I gave Mother Of Pearl its name in the 15th Century , the beauty of Mother Of Pearl has been used in the decoration of jewellery and ornaments since 3000 years before the birth of Christ. The name reflects the fact that shells are the "mother" from which pearls are harvested.

Mother Of Pearl is the smooth lining of iridescent lustre found in some mollusk shells such as large pearl oysters, abalones, pearl mussels and paua shells. Also known as Nacre (from the Arabic word for shell "naqqarah") it is composed of thin layers of calcium carbonate and conchiolin in the form of aragonite or calcite that is secreted by the living mollusk organism.

Carved Mother Of Pearl art

Legends and lore

In the 1920s, a series of tombs were excavated to the east of the site of Babylon in the Middle East. The tombs were of Sumerian Royalty from ancient Mesopotamia and yielded a treasure of gold, silver gemstones and several beautiful wooden ornaments and musical instruments inlaid with Mother Of Pearl (a testament to the sophistication of this ancient culture). The Silver lyre of Ur found in one of the graves in the Royal Cemetery dates back to between 2600 BC and 2400 BC. The lyre was entirely covered in sheet silver and inlaid with Mother Of Pearl.

Just like a butterfly, this Mother Of Pearl pendant displays many colours

A simple, elegant and contemporary design

The Yaqui Indians of Mexico, immortalised in the shamanic tales of Carlos Castaneda, wore a necklace called the "Hopo'orosim". The necklace is made of Mother Of Pearl and is believed to provide the wearer with protection from evil.

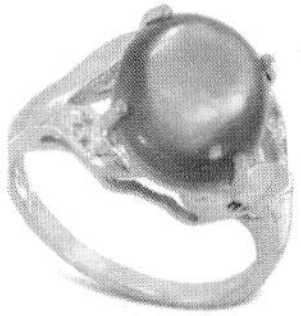

A stunning example of Mother Of Pearl from China, flanked by Diamonds and set in sterling silver

By the 1500s, Europe's growing demand for Mother Of Pearl for use in gold and silver rings, necklaces, brooches and buttons had all but depleted the supplies of Mother Of Pearl in the Persian Gulf.

In 1568, the Solomon Islands, known as "The Pearl of the Pacific", were discovered by the Spanish explorer, Alvaro de Mendana. On discovering the Island's rich bounty of gold and Mother Of Pearl, he gave the archipelago its

Our craftsmen will often shape Mother Of Pearl into various modern shapes

MOTHER OF PEARL

current name, believing that he had found the mythical source of King Solomon's mines.

In Polynesian lore, the iridescence of Mother Of Pearl is attributed to the spirits of coral and sand, Okana and Uaro which, as legend has it, adorned the Tahitian oysters in glistening cloaks covered in all the colours of the fish of the ocean. It is also said that Oro, the Polynesian god of peace and fertility, came down to Earth and offered a special pearl called Te Ufi, the black pearl, to the beautiful princess of Bora Bora, as a sign of his love.

In the 1920s, explorers Sperry and Evans stumbled upon an unusual use for Mother Of Pearl on a remote island of the New Hebrides.

A line of mummies were placed as a barricade, with huge eyes of Mother Of Pearl that shone through the gloom. Amazingly, the mummies weren't ancestral members of the tribe, but were the bodies of a rival tribe of cannibals!

This piece demonstrates how we take our creative inspiration from around the globe

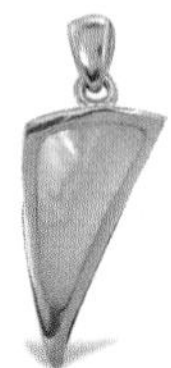

An unusual combination of Mother Of Pearl and Gold which was chosen for its complementary colours

MOTHER OF PEARL:	Produced by mollusk family
Locations:	China, Japan, Australia, Indonesia, Philippines, Tahiti
Colours Found:	White to black
Typical Cuts:	Cabochons, beads, cameos
Family:	Organics
Hardness:	3.00 - 4.50
Refractive Index:	1.52 - 1.65
Relative Density:	2.60 - 2.80

Just the facts

High quality Mother Of Pearl is produced by the mollusk family called bivalves, which have two-part shells.

Mother Of Pearl's Nacre (see also Pearls on page 82) forms when an organic irritant such as a parasite or food-particle becomes trapped within the mollusk, or if the mollusk is injured in some way.

Sensing the object or damage, the living organism within the mollusk secretes calcium carbonate, a derivative mineral of aragonite, and the binding protein conchiolin.

The layers of calcium carbonate settle and are interspersed by the conchiolin, which acts as a kind of organic glue binding the crystals together.

Mother Of Pearl appears in a variety of colours from white to black and nearly every other colour in between. It derives its colour from its genetic make-up, trace metals in the water and, to a lesser extent, the depth and salt content.

Nothing on Earth offers a kaleidoscope of colours quite like Mother Of Pearl.

OBSIDIAN

This gem is supposedly named after Obsidian a Roman said to have brought the first specimens from Lake Shalla, Ethiopia to Rome.

Legends and lore

Today, Obsidian is regarded as one of the most important "teachers" of the New Age movement. Obsidian is said to sharpen both the external and the internal vision. For some crystal healers, it is the warrior of truth, and shows the self where the ego is at, and what it must change in order to advance to the next step of evolutionary growth.

Just the facts

Obsidian is formed by the rapid cooling of viscous lava. It is made of the same minerals as granite but cooled so quickly that they do not have time to crystallise.

Obsidian is usually black, brown or a very dark green, but it can also be found in an almost clear form. It is found in U.S.A, Armenia, Equador, UK, Germany, Guatemala, Hungary, Iceland, Indonesia, Italy, Japan, Mexico, New Zealand, Russia and Slovakia.

Obsidian may be fashioned into a razor sharp cutting edge and ancient civilisations used it not just for jewellery but also to craft cutting tools, such as the sacrificial knives of the Aztecs.

Because of this, Obsidian has been found in locations far from its original source. This might have confused a few gemologists, but it has helped us understand more about the travels of our ancestors.

Today, transparent specimens are faceted, usually into step cuts, while less transparent pieces are fashioned into cabochons.

Especially prized as jewellery, Snowflake Obsidian is a striking, black, lustrous, opaque gem, with white bold markings (formed by internal bubbles or crystals of Potassium Feldspar), much like beautiful patterns of snowflakes on a black background.

Snowflake Obsidian was a big hit with our collectors in 2005.

Australian Snowflake Obsidian set in sterling silver

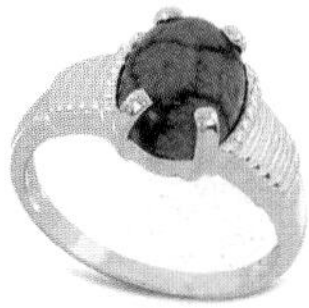

The white colouring in this Snowflake Obsidian is drawn out by the sterling silver setting

A simple pendant that shows the understated elegance of this gem

OBSIDIAN:	Natural glass of volcanic origin
Locations:	India, U. S. A, Armenia, Equator, UK, Germany, Guatemala, Hungry, Iceland, Indonesia, Italy, Japan, Mexico, New Zealand, Russia, Slovakia
Colours Found:	black or a very dark green, almost clear
Typical Cuts:	Cabochon
Family:	Obsidian
Hardness:	5.50 - 7.00
Refractive Index:	1.48 - 1.53
Relative Density:	2.33 - 2.60

ONYX

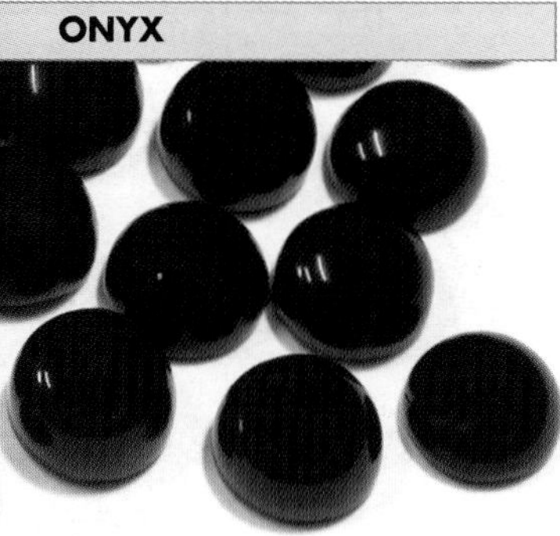

Commonly known as "Black Magic", the name comes from the Greek word "Onyx", which means fingernail or claw. Legend says that one day, while Venus was sleeping, Cupid cut her fingernails and left the clippings scattered on the ground. Because no part of a heavenly body can die, the gods turned them into a gem, which later became known as Onyx.

Legends and lore

In Greek times, almost all colours of Chalcedony from white to dark brown and black were called Onyx. Later, the Romans narrowed the term to refer to black and dark brown colours only. Today when we think of Onyx we often preface the word with black to distinguish it from other varieties. Onyx which is reddish brown and white is known as Sardonyx.

Sardonyx was highly valued in Rome, especially for seals, because it was said to never stick to the wax. Roman General Publius Cornelius Scipio was known for wearing lots of Sardonyx.

Related to its mythological origin, Onyx is believed by some to encourage the growth of fingernails, hair and skin. Onyx is also attributed with ability to soothe ones soul, helping one banish grief and old habits through a better focus. It is also regarded as an extremely protective gem and is widely referenced for its ability to protect against psychic attack.

Sophisticated and elegant gentlemen's jewellery

This pendant shows that Onyx looks stunning in all colours of gold

Just the facts

Onyx is a Chalcedony Quartz with a fine texture and parallel bands of alternate colours.

ONYX:	Consecutive layers of different colours
Locations:	Madagascar, Brazil, India, Uruguay
Colours Found:	Black and white
Typical Cuts:	Cabochons, beads, cameos
Family:	Chalcedony
Hardness:	6.50
Refractive Index:	1.54
Relative Density:	2.59 - 2.61

Our Onyx jewellery

Ideally suited to men, Onyx is associated with instinct and intuition. It is believed to give one the power to deeply analyse a situation before reacting to it, as well as better business acumen and management skills. Crystal healers also believe that it restores confidence in life and love, thereby increasing your happiness.

OPAL

Reportedly, Opal's name evolved from the Roman word "Opalus" and from the Greek word "Opallios" meaning "to see a change of colour". The Greek word was a modification of the ancient Indian Sanskrit name for Opal, "Upala", which meant "Precious Stone". If one spoke in mixed tongues, then Opal would be Opallios Upala, "to see a change of colour precious stone".

Opals are one of the world's most prized gemstones and ancient Greeks valued them more highly than Diamonds. Their body colour covers a broad spectrum of colours, but they are mostly prized for what is known as "play of colour," the ability to reflect and refract light into flashes of multiple colours.

Legends and lore

Historically, Opal was considered a lucky charm that brought beauty, success and happiness to its wearer. The early Greeks believed Opals embodied the powers of foresight and prophecy.

The Romans cherished Opals, considering them a symbol of hope and purity, an appropriate attribute for a gem with a rainbow locked within it. They also used Opals in carvings.

The Arabs thought that Opals must have fallen from heaven in flashes of lightning giving them their unique fiery play of colour or "Opalescence". Members of the Arab community held the belief that Opal would prevent lightning strikes, shield its wearer from any undesirable elements in their day-to-day lives and give a cloak of invisibility to its wearer when desired.

Opal featured in literature, with Shakespeare referring to it in Twelfth Night as "The Queen of Gems".

The history books would have us believe that the European supplies of Opal came from India and the Middle East, but it is far more likely that they came from Hungarian mines.

The antique cut and prong set Multi Colour Opal gives this piece a timeless beauty

This majestic piece contains a 1.4ct Multi Colour Opal mixed with Tsavorite and Diamonds

A 9k gold pendant displaying Opal's natural ability to shimmer

OPAL

Opals made the headlines in the 1890's with the first samples of Australian Opal. The Hungarians declared that the all-new Australian variety was not the real thing. Gems with such a fusion of fire and colour had never been seen before.

Queen Victoria intervened in the near destruction of the 19th Century Opal market when the writer Sir Walter Scott started a superstition that Opals were bad luck for people not born in October. In one of his novels, the heroine owned an Opal that burned fiery red when she was angry and turned ashen grey upon her death. Queen Victoria finally dispelled the curse by giving Opal jewellery as gifts at a royal wedding.

Scandinavian women still wear Opal hair bands to ward off the onset of grey hair and maintain their lustrous blonde locks, while some people believe that this gemstone has therapeutic properties that rejuvenate the inner spirit, invigorating the mind.

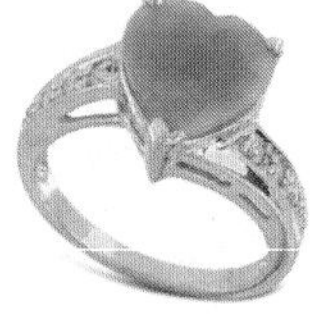

A heart shaped Pink Opal gives this ring its feminine beauty

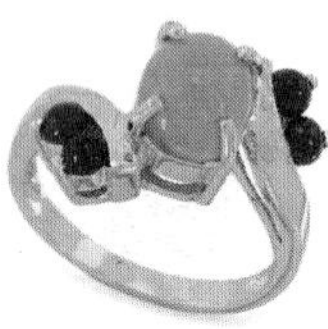

Peruvian Pink Opal paired with Madagascan Rubies

Just the facts

Opals possess a special quality called "Iridescence" or "Opalescence". The effect is similar to the rainbow colours displayed on a soap bubble, only much more dramatic. This rainbow-like effect is also seen in Ammonite and Moonstone.

The physical structure of Opal is unique. Tiny spheres of silicon dioxide form a pyramid-shaped grid interspersed with water. Tiny natural faults in this grid cause the characteristic "play of colour".

A bezel set Blue Opal sits regally in the centre of this gentlemen's ring

Depending on the colour of their "Potch", the host rock on which the Opal formed, Opals will either be classified as Black, Grey, White, Fire and Light, including Crystal and Jelly. Opal actually exhibits many different colours: cherry coloured specimens that rival Ruby, fiery-orange Opals that sparkle like Spessartite Garnet, tropical blue gems as intense as Larimar and even deep gorgeous pinks.

The 9k yellow gold setting helps draw out the different tones in this multi colour Opal

OPAL

Today 95% of the world's Opal is sourced from a handful of prominent mining areas in Australia, namely Lightning Ridge, Coober Pedy, Andamooka and Mintabe.

Black Opal

Black Opal is principally found at Lightning Ridge in New South Wales, Australia. This magnificent gemstone is the most valuable form of Opal. Its dark background colour, usually black, blue, brown or grey, sets the spectral colours ablaze much like a storm cloud behind a rainbow. Black Opal is a gemstone that has had an important effect overseas, as a product of Australia. So valuable is Black Opal that even wafer-thin slices are made into doublets or triplets to give them enough strength and depth to set into gold rings and other jewellery items.

A rare 7.4ct Matrix Opal

Boulder Opal

Boulder Opal is found sparsely distributed over a wide area of Australian ironstone or boulder country, where the Opal infills cracks and crevices in the ironstone boulders. Opal bearing boulder is always cut, including the host brown ironstone. Boulder Opal is in very high demand and extremely precious. Boulder Opal is usually cut to the contours of the Opal vein, creating a baroque, wavy surface and is often freeform and irregular in shape, making boulder Opal unique.

A valuable Australian Black Opal made into a simple pendant

Crystal Opal

Crystal Opal is transparent and is pure Opal (hydrated silica). It typically has sharp clarity of diffracted colour visible from within and on the surfaces of the Opal. When held out of the direct light, Crystal Opal displays some of the most intense Opal colour. This is the type of Opal used in Opal inlay jewellery, which has the base of the setting blackened before the precision cut crystal Opal is set into it.

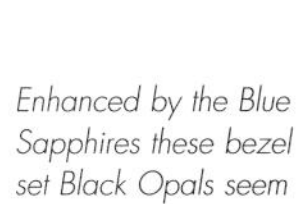

Enhanced by the Blue Sapphires these bezel set Black Opals seem to glow

White Opal

White Opal is the most common type of precious Opal and is translucent, with a creamy appearance which dominates the diffracted colours. All of the Australian Opal fields produce White Opal with most of it being mined in Coober Pedy.

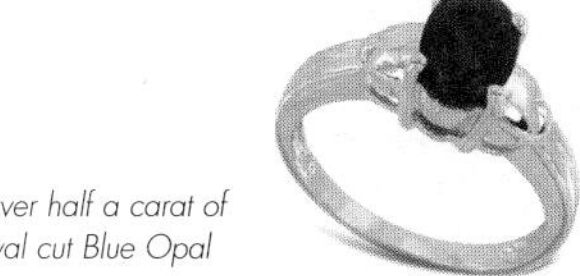

Over half a carat of oval cut Blue Opal

OPAL

The octagon cut of this Fire Opal enhances the natural lustre of this gem

An effortlessly elegant pendant containing 8 marquise cut Fire Opals

The deep 9k gold prong setting of this ring accentuates the lustre of this Blue Opal

Mexican Fire Opal

Mexican Fire Opals are a remarkable variety, offering deep tangerine hues that have been treasured in the Americas since Aztec days. Mexican Fire Opal is mostly found in extinct volcanoes and is threaded and veined with opaline rock. The gem is normally hidden in niches and caves and is generally mined above the surface.

Jelly Opal

Jelly Opal (also known as Water Opal) is predominately mined in Mexico. Jelly Opal offers an attractive blend of indistinct, fuzzy colours. It is transparent, with a gelatinous appearance and an occasional bluish sheen. The "play of colour" is a subtle sheen of colour dancing through the gem, rather than colour patches. Very occasionally, it is also found in Lightning Ridge, Australia, where it is essentially Black Opal without the black potch background.

Peruvian Opal

Peruvian Opal hailing from the Andes, is extremely rare and exhibits exquisite translucent colouring. Favoured by the ancient Incas, it typically comes in subtle blue or pink colours.

Fire Opal

Fire Opal is also found in Honduras or Guatemala, in the U.S.A, Canada, Australia and Turkey. However, in most of these countries, finds are too small to make it financially viable to mine.

Of all the Opal taken out of the ground, 95% is valueless "potch" and 95% of the remainder is low quality. Only a mere 0.25% ever makes it into jewellery. With such an incredibly small yield and because many of the locations where

What our Craftsmen say:

Mr.Sangkhom Phokhanit - Jeweller

"Fire Opal's colour is simply breathtaking. As we set this popular gem into rings, pendants and bracelets, why not invoke your inner diva with the fashion-forward style of Fire Opal."

OPAL

it is mined are in regions where labour costs are very high, it starts to become clear why Opal demands such a high price.

Opals From Lightning Ridge, Australia

Opals are one of Australia's national treasures, and one of the world's most prized gemstones.

Lightning Ridge is 600 miles north of Sydney, and is the only place on Earth where the king of Opals, "The Black Opal", is found.

The Black Opal mining fields of Lightning Ridge and the majority of Australia's Opal fields are located in a geological phenomenon called "The Great Australian Basin". The Basin was formed from sediments of a large inland sea that existed over 140 million years ago.

120 Million years later, sandstones were deposited by waterways over the top of these sedimentary rocks. Eventually, these younger rocks weathered, and their silica filtered down to cavities in the older host rock in the form of a gel.

An oval cut vivid Blue Opal

The silica gel hardened, forming around a nucleus, creating the Opal's characteristic regular spheres and voids. It's the diffraction of light through these transparent spaces that produces Opal's brilliant play of colours.

A breath-taking Semi-Black Opal stunningly enhanced by the 9k white gold setting

Opal mining involves hard digging with picks and shovels 6-18 metres underground. Buckets are then loaded and hauled to the surface using simple mechanical winches. The material is then separated by hand, separating out the larger rocks then reducing it further by hand sieving.

The remainder of the gem-rich material is taken to small converted cement mixers, which wash off the excess dirt from the "Nobbies" (rough Opal).

With "the fire of the carbuncle, the brilliant purple of the Amethyst, the sea green colours of Emerald all shining together in incredible union" Opal clearly impressed Pliny the Elder (23-79 AD), Roman historian and author of the world's first encyclopedia.

If you are looking to be impressed with Opals there is no better place to start building your collection than on Gems TV!

OPAL:	October's birthstone
Locations:	Australia, Peru, Mexico,Tanzania, Zimbabwe, South Africa, Brazil, Indonesia
Colours Found:	Multiple
Typical Cuts:	All cuts
Family:	Opal
Hardness:	5.50 - 6.50
Refractive Index:	1.73 - 1.46
Relative Density:	1.80 - 2.30

PEARL

Pearls are the oldest known gem and, for centuries, were considered the most valuable. So valuable, in fact, that the Roman General Vitellius allegedly financed an entire military campaign with just one of his mother's Pearl earrings!

The days of island inhabitants free diving into bottomless, azure oceans to harvest Pearls are more or less over. Natural, uncultured Pearls are extremely expensive and are very rarely seen in today's jewellery. Nowadays they tend only to make appearances as antiques.

Legends and lore

The Romans were particularly enamoured with this gem of the sea and Rome's Pearl craze reached its zenith during the 1st Century BC, when upper class Roman women (the lower ranks were forbidden from wearing them) wore their Pearls to bed so they could be reminded of their wealth immediately upon awakening. They also upholstered couches with Pearls and sewed so many into their gowns that they actually walked on their Pearl-encrusted hems. The famously excessive Emperor Caligula, having made his beloved horse a Consul, decorated it with a Pearl necklace.

An impressive 20ct pin set Pearl

Cleopatra, in describing her enormous wealth and power, demonstrated to Marc Anthony how she could "drink the wealth of nations" by crushing Pearls into a glass of wine.

9k gold, Diamonds and delicate Chinese Pearls blended together in this graceful looking pendant

The first known source of Pearls was the Persian Gulf and the ancients of the area believed that Pearls were a symbol of the moon and had magical powers. Indeed, the oldest known Pearl jewellery is a necklace found in the sarcophagus of a Persian princess who died in 520 BC.

Flanked by Diamonds, the Pearl gives the ring a magical quality

The earliest written record of their value is in the Shu King, a 23rd Century BC Chinese book in which the scribe sniffs that a lesser king sent a tribute of "strings of Pearls not quite round". The Chinese also used Pearls in medicinal ways to cure eye ailments, heart trouble, indigestion, fever and bleeding. To this day, Pearl powder is still popular in China as a skin whitener and cosmetic.

In India, Pearls were believed to give peace of mind and strength of body and soul.

Europeans thought that swallowing whole or powdered Pearls cured matters of the mind and heart and strengthened nerves.

While Queen Isabella had to hock her impressive collection of jewellery to fund Christopher Columbus' expedition to discover the New World, the investment paid off as the discovery of Pearls in Central American waters added to the wealth of Spain. The flood of American Pearls onto the European market earned the newly discovered continent the nickname "Land of Pearls". Unfortunately, greed and lust for these gems of the sea resulted in the depletion of virtually all the American Pearl oyster populations by the 17th Century.

During the Dark Ages, while fair maidens of nobility cherished delicate Pearl necklaces, gallant knights often wore Pearls onto the battlefield. They believed that the magic possessed by the lustrous gems would protect them from harm.

Pearls have long been considered ideal wedding gifts because they symbolise purity and innocence. In the Hindu religion, the presentation of an un-drilled Pearl and its piercing has formed part of the marriage ceremony. While, in the Western hemisphere, Pearls are the recommended gift for couples celebrating their 3rd and 30th wedding anniversaries.

Just the facts

The Natural Pearl begins life as a foreign body, a grain of sand or coral, which makes its way into the shell of a marine or freshwater mollusk – usually oysters or clams. The mollusk's defense mechanism starts to coat the intruder with layers of a slightly iridescent substance "Nacre", which is the attractive outside of the Pearl. In its natural environment this will, after many years, form a Pearl that is of a significant size and quality to be of commercial value.

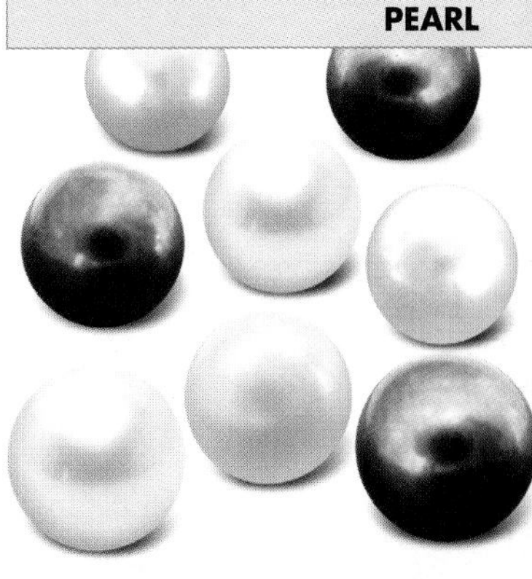

The Aquamarine gems set into the shoulders of this ring bring out the blue tones in this Pearl

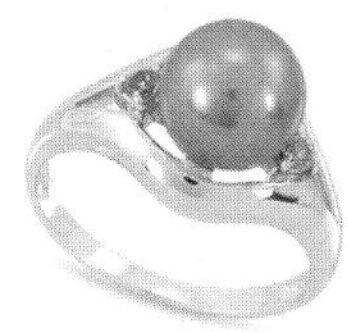

A delicate Pink Pearl set into 9k white gold

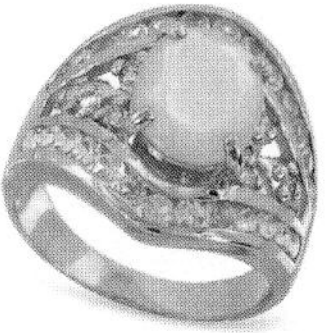

This Pearl's yellow hues are enhanced by the 9k gold setting in this gentlemen's ring

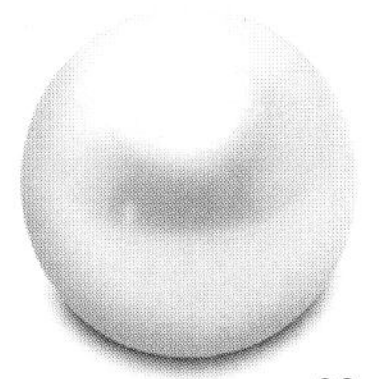

PEARL

Unlike Natural Pearls, cultivated Pearls do not begin as accidental intruders. The process starts with "Nucleation". A cultivated Pearl begins its life when a spherical Mother Of Pearl bead is placed inside the mollusk. After this seeding process, the Pearl farmers place the oysters in wire-mesh baskets and suspend them in the sea. The aqua-culturists carefully tend to the oysters, overseeing their development for a period of anything from 18 months to 3 years, eventually producing high quality Pearls. The depth of the Nacre coating, an important factor when estimating the value of Pearls, depends on how long the seeded Pearls are left in place before being harvested.

As with all things natural, Pearls can only grow in the right conditions. The first thing to consider is the provenance of the Pearl. Different Pearl varieties from different locations command different prices. The best quality Pearls are found in the Asian waters of Tahiti, Japan and China. However, due to the different environments, mollusk species and production techniques, all cultivated Pearls have their own distinctive qualities.

Freshwater Pearls are cultured by slightly different methods without a bead. Although historically originating in Japan, China is a now a major producer of Freshwater Pearls. Chinese Freshwater Pearls are cultured in the Yangtze River using, not oysters, but freshwater clams. The humble clam, while not as widely celebrated as its cousin the oyster, is equally capable of producing high quality Pearls.

While Pearls are classified as coloured gems, there is a unique appeal about them. Unlike other gemstones that are born of earth and fire, Pearls are water born organic gems that originate from living animals. They are also unique in the sense that the principles of the 4 Cs (colour, cut, clarity and carat) cannot be applied to them. The evaluation of Pearls requires a different set of criteria. A Pearl's value is appraised according to the display of colour, lustre, surface clarity, shape and size as well their "Orient".

The dark tones of this unusual Pearl are perfectly complemented by the Colour Change Sapphires on the shoulders

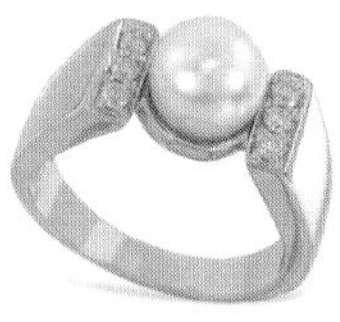

Another example of the always brilliant pairing of Diamonds and Pearls

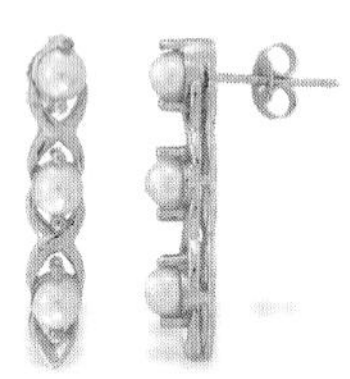

These elegant earrings contain 6 Japanese Pearls

A timelessly elegant ring featuring a Chinese Pearl and Diamonds

PEARL

Apart from the obvious body colour (white, cream, pink, gold, silver-grey and black), there is actually a second colour to consider when evaluating Pearls. This second colour is actually a result of subtle iridescence. While not instantly obvious, especially when similar to the body colour, this effect lends Pearls much of their allure and beauty. Typically, this iridescence is seen most strongly on the crest of a Pearl's horizon. This beautiful, shimmering effect is known as the "Orient" or overtone and denotes the depth of the Nacre. Pearls with rich colourful Orients are generally valued higher than those that have little or no Orient.

Chinese Pearls consist almost entirely of Nacre and will often exhibit a distinct rainbow Orient. However, Japanese Akoya Pearls, due to their very thin layers of nacre (3-5%), will rarely show orient. By contrast, the Tahitian Black Pearl, cultured using the Japanese method, will exhibit orient. Why? Because the nacre coating is in excess of two millimetres, thick enough to allow light to reflect.

As with other gemstones, value and weight are intrinsically linked, the heavier the Pearl, the greater it's desirability. However, there is one important difference; Pearls are often measured and expressed by their size not weight (e.g. 8.5mm).

Debby Cavill

Gems TV's Chief of Global Jewellery Design

"We take a lot of our inspiration when designing Pearl jewellery by admiring many of the designs worn by the rich and famous. I recently read a book called "Elizabeth Taylor My Love Affair With Jewellery". One of her favoured gems is the Pearl. Her collection includes historic pieces such as "La Peregrian" through to a beautiful strand of cultured Pearls. My favourite Pearl earrings (that weren't made by us), were also worn by Elizabeth Taylor to the 1960 Academy Awards - I wasn't born then but have seen photos. They were Cultured South Sea Pearls, very similar to the ones we set and were surrounded by 64 Diamonds! She was also featured wearing them on the front cover of Life Magazine. Elizabeth said "These earrings started me on my love of long, drippy earrings".

Where pink and Pearls meet, there are always admirers from every culture and corner of the globe

Gorgeous Cultured Pearls from China are fast becoming a fashion trend in the UK

Chinese Cultured Pearls beautifully displaying a distinct rainbow coloured Orient

PEARL:	June's birthstone
Locations:	China, Japan, Australia, Indonesia, Philippines, Tahiti
Colours Found:	White, cream, pink, gold, black, grey, silver, orange, golden-yellow
Typical Cuts:	Ornaments, beads
Family:	Organics
Hardness:	3.00 - 4.00
Refractive Index:	1.53 - 1.68
Relative Density:	2.60 - 2.78

PERIDOT

Called the "gem of the sun" by Ancient Egyptians and the "evening Emerald" by Romans, Peridot was a favourite gemstone of Cleopatra and was frequently mistaken for Emerald. The pronunciation of this popular gem is often confused and should be pronounced pair-ee-doh, as opposed to pair-ee-dot.

Legends and lore

Common in early Greek and Roman jewellery, Peridot has been popular since 1500 BC, when the Egyptians started mining it on Zeberget, later known as St. John's Island, about 50 miles off the Egyptian coast in the Red Sea.

Peridot mining was traditionally done at night when the gem's natural glow is easier to see, the ancient Egyptians even believed that Peridots became invisible under the sun's rays.

Hawaiian natives believe Peridot is the goddess Pele's tears, while biblical references to the gem include the High Priest's breastplate - studded with a stone for each of the twelve tribes of Israel, one being Peridot.

Cleopatra reportedly had a fine collection of "Emerald" jewellery, which was really Peridot.

The Ottoman Sultans gathered the largest collection during their 600 year reign from 1300-1918, with an impressive array of both loose gemstones as well as Peridot earrings, Peridot rings and other Peridot jewellery.

Powdered Peridot has been used to cure asthma and a Peridot placed under the tongue of someone in the grip of a fever was believed to lessen their thirst. Legend has it that drinking from a Peridot goblet can increase the potency of medicines.

Pirates believed Peridot had the power to drive away evil spirits (and the night's terrors), especially if set in gold. But, as protection from evil spirits, they believed it must be pierced, strung on donkey hair and worn on the left arm.

Possibly the most unusual Peridot is that which comes from meteorites called Pallasites. Some have been faceted and set in jewellery, one of the few extraterrestrial gemstones known to man.

The unusual "cut-out" shoulders of this ring accentuate this dazzling 3.4ct Peridot

Simple pear cut Peridot set into 9k gold

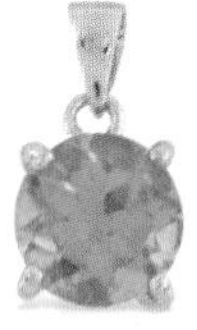

This simple pendant boldly displays Peridot's characteristic lustre

PERIDOT

Just the facts

Peridot is a gem variety of Forsterite-Olivine, which exhibits golden lime-greens and rich grass-greens.

Coloured by iron, Peridot is an idiochromatic gem meaning that its colour is an essential part of its composition - unlike gems such as Ruby or Sapphire that are coloured by trace elements present as impurities.

Because of the way Peridot splits and bends the rays of light passing through it, it has a velvety, "sleepy" appearance - a shining rich glow, and a slightly greasy lustre.

The purer green a Peridot is, the higher the value. The green hues of Peridot vary in colour from rich grass-like greens reminiscent of Emeralds and Tsavorite, to yellowish greens that may, at times, have hints of brown.

Peridot is found in several places around the world, but interestingly not in nearly as many locales as Diamonds or Sapphire, technically making it rarer!

In 1994, an exciting new deposit of Peridot was discovered in Pakistan, and these stones are among the finest ever seen.

The new mine is located 15,000 feet above sea level in the Nanga Parbat region in the far west of the Himalayan Mountains in the Pakistani port of Kashmir. Beautiful large crystals of Peridot have been found there and one gem was once reported to be more than 300cts!

This modern six prong setting gives the ring a contemporary sophistication

Our highly skilled gemcutters highlight the brilliance inside this dazzling Peridot

A beautifully cut Peridot with fantastic colouring

Gavin "Gemstone Gav" Linsell says:

"Imagine sitting on a royal lawn, basking in the mid summer heat. The beautiful, vivid, slightly golden shimmering green of Peridot is the perfect gem to go with any summer outfit. Even after sunset when one enters indoors, the brilliant green sparkle of Peridot still magically dances and sings under artificial light. Is it really a coincidence that it is the official Birthstone of August?"

PERIDOT:	August's birthstone
Locations:	Pakistan, China, U.S.A
Colours Found:	Rich grass-like green, yellowish greens
Typical Cuts:	All cuts
Family:	Olivine
Hardness:	6.50
Refractive Index:	1.64 - 1.69
Relative Density:	3.34

QUARTZ

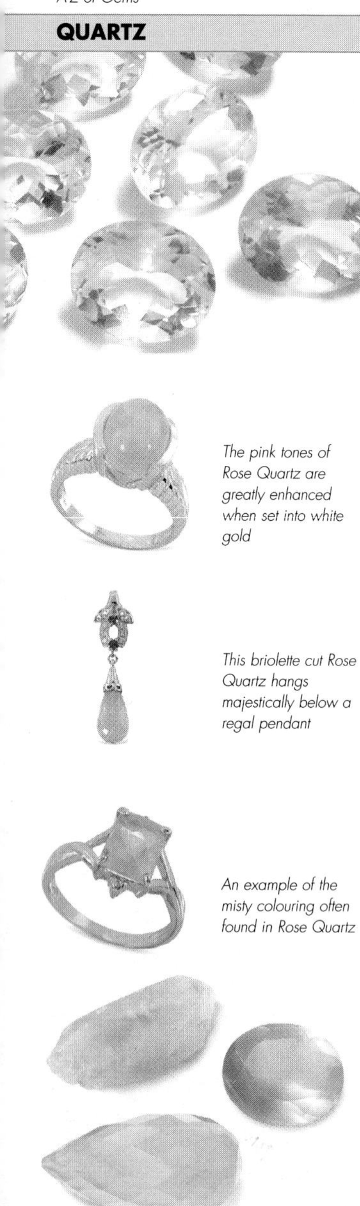

The pink tones of Rose Quartz are greatly enhanced when set into white gold

This briolette cut Rose Quartz hangs majestically below a regal pendant

An example of the misty colouring often found in Rose Quartz

The Greeks originally named Quartz "Krystallos" meaning "Ice", but this term was soon applied to any crystal. In fact, the modern name of Quartz is derived from the Saxon word "Querklufterz" meaning "cross vein ore".

One of Earth's most abundant minerals, Quartz is also one of the most interesting! It makes up about 12% of the Earth's crust, occurring in a wide variety of rocks. Gem quality varieties of Quartz have been used in jewellery and other ornamental objects for thousands of years.

Due to its electric properties, it is used as a radio component and is utilised in watches and clocks where a tiny Quartz plate is used to control precisely the radio frequency of the electronic circuitry.

Legends and lore

The ancients of India considered Quartz to have special properties as transformers as well as keepers of energy.

To this day Quartz crystals are used universally in meditation, as they are believed to possess healing properties and other diverse metaphysical powers.

Folklorists classify Quartz as a receptive gemstone credited with the ability to attract positive energies, such as peace and love. The subtle energy of Quartz is said to balance the emotions, giving inner peace, harmony and enhancing the bonds of relationships. It is also said to calm aggression and increase self-esteem.

Just the facts

Quartz varieties are commonly separated into two groups based on the size of the individual grains or crystals:

Macrocrystalline Quartz is when individual crystals are distinguishable with the naked eye. Some of the Macrocrystalline Quartz varieties are Amethyst, Green Amethyst, Ametrine, Tiger's Eye, Citrine, Rock Crystal, Rose Quartz, Rutilated Quartz and Smoky Quartz.

QUARTZ

Cryptocrystalline Quartz is when the individual crystals are too small to be easily distinguishable under a 10x loupe. Chalcedony (also spelled Calcedony) is a catch-all term to describe these varieties and includes Agate (banded varieties), Carnelian (red to reddish brown), Sard (light to dark brown), Chrysoprase (apple green), Bloodstone (green with red spots), Jasper (generally red but sometimes yellow, brown, green and grey blue) and Flint (dull grey to black).

Phenomena sometimes observed in Quartz include asterism (star effect) and chatoyancy (cat's eye effect).

Prasiolite is a confusing gem as it is traded under a variety of names and can easily be mistaken for other gem types. Prasiolite, also known as Green Amethyst, is quite simply Green Quartz.

Smoky Quartz is brown transparent Quartz of all shades and generally has a slightly greyish cast. Also known as "Champagne On Ice", Smoky Quartz is an earth-toned transparent Quartz that gets its rich warm colour from aluminium. A variety of Smoky Quartz is Cairngorm, which owes its name to the legendary source in Scotland. Smoky Quartz is the national gem of Scotland, whose national sceptre includes a large Smoky Quartz on its top.

Rock Crystal is colourless Quartz.

Rose Quartz is the pink variety of Quartz; it is rarely transparent. Facet grade material will usually be a bit "misty" in appearance. Rose Quartz is set both in precious jewellery and in gem necklaces.

Rutile Quartz is colourless, displaying golden needle-like inclusions that appear as long threads forming intriguing natural patterns.

Tiger's Eye is a beautiful Chatoyant Quartz.

Star Quartz is a fascinating gem that clearly displays asterism (star effect) and is either colourless or pink. The stars are six-rayed and roll around the gem as it is moved.

The exceptional design of this piece expertly draws your eye to the central Smoky Quartz

The majesty of 6.6cts of striking Brazilian Smoky Quartz

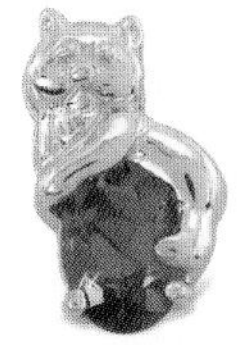

Another expert piece designed with our youngest customers in mind

QUARTZ:	Makes up about 12% of the Earth's crust
Locations:	Brazil, Madagascar, Mozambique, South Africa, U.S.A, Sri Lanka, Mexico, France
Colours Found:	Red to reddish brown, dark brown, apple green, green with red spots, red sometimes yellow, brown, green and grey blue, dull grey to black
Typical Cuts:	All cuts
Family:	Quartz
Hardness:	7.00
Refractive Index:	1.50
Relative Density:	2.60 - 2.65

RHODOCHROSITE

A massive 26cts of Rhodochrosite and 20 Diamonds went into creating this contemporary and feminine pendant

The brilliant red colour of this 32ct Rhodochrosite is simply breathtaking

RHODOCHROSITE:	Perfect cleavage
Locations:	Brazil, Australia, Namibia, South Africa, U.S.A, Argentina, Peru, Brazil, Russia, Mexico, Canada
Colours Found:	Red to pink, sometimes white, yellow, brown
Typical Cuts:	Cabochon, pear
Family:	Calcite
Hardness:	3.50 - 4.50
Refractive Index:	1.60 - 1.80
Relative Density:	3.40 - 3.70

Rhodochrosite (whose name means rose-coloured from the Greek words "Rhodon", rose and "Chroma", colour) is a very attractive gem with an absolutely beautiful colour.

Legends and lore

Rhodochrosite is believed by crystal healers to be a gemstone of love and balance for emotions and male/female energies and assists in expanding consciousness, and healing Mother Earth.

Rhodochrosite was a popular ornamental stone during the 1930s and was often carved into decorative objects like figurines. Bands can be pink and red, as well as pink and white.

Just the facts

Rhodochrosite is a Manganese Carbonate with a vivid pink-rose and red colour derived from Manganese. Some fine crystals of Rhodochrosite are cut into gems, but this is difficult because of the perfect cleavage. As a result, Rhodochrosite is often cut and polished as cabochons.

Rhodochrosite occurs in hydrothermal mineral veins containing ores of silver, lead and copper. Individual crystals are found in Rhombohedrons and sometimes Scalehedrons, but large crystals are rare.

Rhodochrosite ranges from very pale pink, pale to deep red, orange red, brownish red, orange-brown, pale to dark brown and black.

Rhodochrosite is found in a number of locations worldwide. For several years now the Sweet Home Mine in Alma and the Sunnyside Mine in Silverton, Colorado have been mined exclusively for Rhodochrosite specimens. The Hotazel Mine in South Africa is famous for producing deep red clusters of Rhodochrosite crystals.

However, the most famous mines are in the provinces of Catamarca and La Rioja, Argentina. The mines there produce an attractive pink and red banded Rhodochrosite, that is sometimes referred to as 'Inca Rose'.

RUBELLITE

Rubellite, deriving its name from the Latin word "Rubellus" meaning "coming from red" is a lustrous, reddish pink and purple toned variety of Tourmaline. Extremely rare, Rubellite has taken the jewellery world by storm, often exhibiting more beauty than Ruby.

Legends and lore

The Dutch, aside from admiring its beauty, first discovered that the gem possessed a unique property. Rubellite (Pink Tourmaline) when heated or rubbed creates an electrical charge becoming a magnet that attracts lightweight objects.

The Dutch used these magnets to clean pipes as their magnetic properties attracted ash, and renamed Tourmaline "Aschentrekkers", literally meaning "one who treks through ashes."

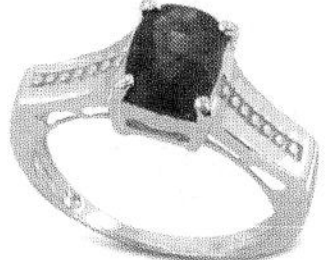

Another distinctive design from our expert designers

In the 17th Century, the Tsar of Russia commissioned many items of gemstone jewellery to be made for the Imperial Crown Court. However, recently, what were originally thought to be Rubies, in reality, have been discovered to be Rubellite Tourmalines.

Octagon cut Rubellite set into 9k gold paired with Tanzanite

Another monarch enchanted by Tourmaline was the Empress Dowager Tz'u Hsi, the last Empress of China. She loved Tourmaline so much that she bought almost a ton of it, even going to her eternal resting place on a pillow carved from Rubellite. During the Manchu Dynasty in China, members of the Mandarin class wore round buttons made of Rubellite Tourmaline, distinguishing themselves from other classes of citizens.

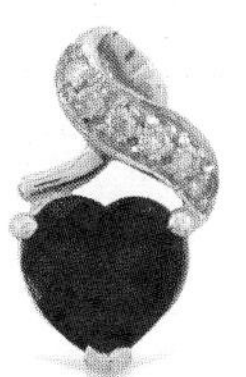

This feminine pendant features a twist of pave set Diamonds above a heart shaped Rubellite

Just the facts

Rubellite that exhibits a deep ruby red colour is rather rare and is by far the most valuable form of Tourmaline. Like Emerald, inclusions in Rubellite are common. The chemical impurities that colour Rubellite red or pink actually cause a growing crystal to become internally flawed or cracked. The more the impurity is present, the darker the red colour and the more imperfect the final crystal. It is therefore extremely rare to find dark violet, pink or red Rubellite that is 'clean' internally.

Perfectly matched cushion cut Rubellite

RUBELLITE

The noble lustre of this gem shows why it has been so popular with royalty through the ages

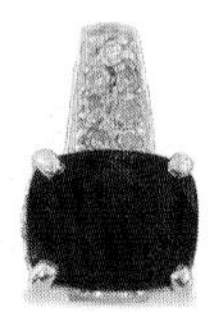

This pendant demonstrates why the cushion cut is the favoured cut of Rubellite

RUBELLITE:	Colour is close to pigeon blood rubies
Locations:	Madagascar, Nigeria, Tanzania, Brazil
Colours Found:	Passionate pinks, opulence of red, change colour from reddish pink to purple
Typical Cuts:	All Cuts, ornamentals, carvings
Family:	Tourmaline
Hardness:	7.00 - 7.50
Refractive Index:	1.62 - 1.64
Relative Density:	3.03 - 3.10

Like any other colour of Tourmaline, Rubellite displays pleochroism meaning that its colour changes when viewed at different angles. However, this can vary from specimen to specimen.

In some, this effect is hardly noticeable, while in others it is strongly apparent. Gemstone cutters must take this into account when cutting a Rubellite to bring out its best colour.

With the exception of Ruby and its frequent imitator Noble Red Spinel, Rubellite is the only other gemstone that occurs in such a rich, dark-red colour. Interestingly, Rubellite frequently exhibits more beauty and sparkle than its more expensive look-a-like.

Rubellite crystals occur in granite pegmatite veins occurring in the great gem mining districts of Minas Gerias in Brazil, Nigeria, Tanzania, and Madagascar.

In the summer of 1998 a new deposit was unearthed near the city of Ibadan in Nigeria, West Africa, proving to be one of the most significant discoveries in modern times.

Our Rubellite jewellery

Rubellite's sensuous mélange is the personification of seduction, no other colours display comparable feminine flair. Whispering in passionate pinks and suggestive purples, Rubellite affords the perfect romance in an opulence of red. Once aware of the extravagance and beauty of this gemstone, a woman can not be parted from her Rubellite.

Our design team refer to Rubellite as the most feminine of gems. Even though it tends to be a highly included gem, it's beauty is undeniable.

When we are able to fashion large carat weights, they make beautiful solitaire rings and pendants.

When larger carat weights are unavailable our designers will create half eternity rings and stunning earrings.

RUBY

Ruby derives its name from the Latin word for red, "Rufus". The beauty, rarity and historical mystique of Rubies are undeniable. Ruby is the anniversary gemstone for 15 and 40 years of marriage and is said to bring particularly good luck to gamblers and lovers.

Legends and lore

With the earliest record for the mining of Rubies dating from more than 2,500 years ago, the historical mystique and beauty of Rubies is as colourful as the legends and lore that surround this most precious of gems.

Prized throughout history, many believed that mystical powers lay hidden within this intensely coloured red gemstone. Furthermore, the fiery crimson colour of Rubies caused many civilisations to associate them with passion, love and romance. Rubies were also thought to bestow wisdom, health and luck in gambling.

The king of gems gives this traditional pendant a glamourous edge

Mentioned in Sanskrit texts, the ancient Hindus were so enchanted by the colour of Rubies that they called them Rajnapura "The King Of Gems". The ancient Hindus thought that the colours of Rubies were due to an inextinguishable fire that burned inside the gem, which would endow it's wearer with long life and even cause water to boil!

A dazzling 3.6ct Ruby is the centerpiece of this eye-catching ring

As in Sanskrit texts, Biblical references to Ruby (all red gemstones were collectively called Carbuncle at this time) refer to it as a most precious gem. Interestingly, the gems called "Rubies" in the Old Testament may have actually been red Spinels or Garnets. Up until the 18th Century, when chemical testing was improved, most red gems were called Rubies.

A sophisticated bracelet created with 33 bar set Rubies deftly displays their natural brilliance

In the King James Version of the Bible, Ruby (i.e. Carbuncle) is mentioned four times:

Exodus 28:17

And thou shalt set in it settings of stones, even four rows of stones: the first row shall be a Sardius, a Topaz, and a Carbuncle: this shall be the first row.

Exodus 39:10

And they set in it four rows of stones: the first

Twenty channel set Rubies accentuate the contemporary appeal of this striking ring

RUBY

Rubies are always a popular choice with men

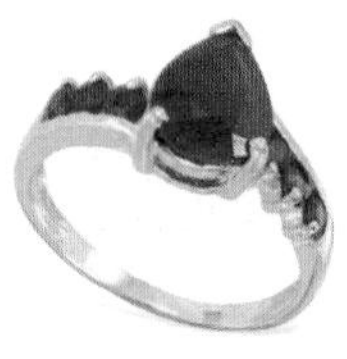

A very striking ring made up of only rubies and 9k gold

A captivating round cut Ruby surrounded by Diamonds

The gem of love aptly faceted in a traditional heart shape

row was a Sardius, a Topaz, and a Carbuncle: this was the first row.

Ezekiel 28:13

Thou hast been in Eden the garden of God; every precious stone was thy covering, the Sardius, Topaz, and the Diamond, the Beryl, the Onyx, and the Jasper, the Sapphire, the Emerald, and the Carbuncle, and Gold: the workmanship of thy tabrets and of thy pipes was prepared in thee in the day that thou wast created.

Isaiah 54:12

And I will make thy windows of Agates, and thy gates of Carbuncles, and all thy borders of pleasant stones.

In fact, many of the famous "Rubies" in the crown jewels of Europe have since been identified as red Spinels or Garnets. For example, the Black Prince Ruby that rests proudly at the centre of the British Imperial State Crown is actually a red Spinel!

Ancient Ceylonese legends (modern day Sri Lanka) relate the story of the destruction of their demonic King Ravana. They believed that after his demise, his blood set into Rubies resulting in their intense red colour.

Native Americans believed that offerings of a fine Ruby resulted in rebirth as a powerful Chief.

Some cultures believed Ruby's blood-like colour would protect the wearer from injury. In fact, ancient Burmese warriors believed that when a Ruby was inserted beneath the skin it generated a mystical force, making them unconquerable in battle.

In the 13th Century, the renowned explorer Marco Polo wrote that Kublai Kahn, the Mongol Emperor of China, once offered an entire city for a Ruby the size of a man's finger.

Because of its fluorescent properties, a giant Ruby once lit an entire chamber in a palace of a Chinese Emperor!

In the Middle Ages, Rubies were thought to contain prophetic powers. It was believed that a Ruby could warn its owner of misfortunes by deepening in colour.

RUBY

Just the facts

Apart from their colour, Rubies are identical to Sapphires. Rubies and Sapphires are comprised of the mineral known as Corundum.

Did you know that Rubies are rarer than Diamonds? In the last 60 years hardly a month has passed without a new Diamond deposit being discovered. In contrast, Rubies are only found in a handful of mines worldwide.

Did you know that Rubies are more expensive than Diamonds? A 16ct Ruby that sold at Sotheby's in New York in October 1988 fetched a staggering $3,630,000.

Second only to Diamonds in hardness, Rubies are one of the toughest gemstones and with no cleavage, breakage rarely occurs. This, combined with the fact that Rubies come in many different shapes and sizes, makes them perfect for all types of jewellery.

Microscopic inclusions, commonly known as "Silk", are a normal characteristic of Rubies. Evenly distributed small quantities of "Silk" act like fine dust, creating a soft, uniform distribution of light throughout the Ruby, enhancing it's beauty.

Our Ruby jewellery

We source our Rubies from Vietnam, Kenya, Tanzania, Sri Lanka, China and of course our home country of Thailand. While Thai gemstone deposits were previously some of the biggest in the world, strict environmental regulations combined with depletion has seen mining greatly reduced.

With approximately 80% of the world's Rubies passing through Chanthaburi (the home town of the Gems TV design centre in Thailand), our craftspeople are the first to choose the finest examples of this gem of passion, love and romance. We use Rubies when handcrafting all manner of gorgeous jewellery, and being the gem of love, heart shaped Rubies are hard to resist.

On average, we introduce around five new Ruby designs everyday! So next time you need a bit of passion in your life, tune into Gems TV.

An unusual mix of cuts, sizes and origins make for unique Ruby pendant

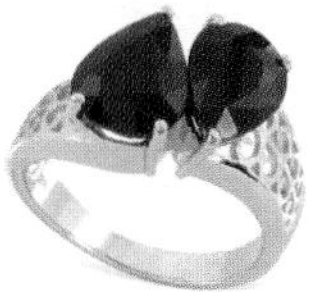

The remarkable deep red hues of these Rubies are delightfully accentuated when set into 9k white gold

RUBY:	July's birthstone
Locations:	Madagascar, Tanzania, Kenya, Thailand, Vietnam, China, India
Colours Found:	Intense red
Typical Cuts:	All cuts
Family:	Corundum
Hardness:	9.00
Refractive Index:	1.76 - 1.77
Relative Density:	3.90 - 4.10

SAPPHIRE

Another beautifully vintage looking piece containing 7 Sapphires

This stunning 6ct cabochon cut Sapphire is coupled with 30 pave set Diamonds

Inspired designs and stunning gemstones are our speciality

Sapphires derived their name from the Latin word "sapphirus", meaning "blue", and are often referred to as the "gem of the heavens" or the "celestial gem" as their colours mirror the sky at different the times of day.

The word Sapphire, stated without a prefix, implies Blue Sapphire only. Sapphires of all other colours are assigned a colour prefix or are collectively termed "Fancy Sapphires".

Legends and lore

Legend has it that the first person to wear Sapphire was Prometheus, the rival of Zeus, who took the gemstone from Cacaus, where he also stole fire from heaven for man.

The Ancient Greeks adorned themselves with Sapphires when consulting the oracles at the temple of the Greek god Apollo in Delphi. The Ancient Persians believed Sapphires were a chip from the pedestal that supported the Earth, and that its reflections gave the sky its colours.

Sapphire was one of the 12 holy gemstones set into the breastplate of the high priest Aaron, documented in the Exodus book of the Bible.

The guardians of innocence, Sapphires symbolise truth, sincerity and faithfulness and are thought to bring peace, joy and wisdom to their owners. In ancient times, it was believed that when the wearer of a Sapphire faced challenging obstacles, the gem's power enabled them to find the correct solution.

In India, it was believed that a Sapphire immersed in water formed an elixir that could cure the bite of scorpions and snakes. Alternatively, if it were worn as a talisman pendant, it would protect the wearer against evil spirits.

The following legend is Burmese in origin and highlights Sapphire's connection with faithfulness: "Eons ago, Tsun-Kyan-Kse, a golden haired goddess with Sapphire blue eyes, presided lovingly over the temple of Lao-Tsun. Everyday, the temple's chief monk Mun-Ha, meditated before the golden goddess accompanied by his devoted companion, a green-eyed cat named Sinh. One day, the temple was besieged by a group of terrible outlaws. When they threw Mun-Ha to the floor, Sinh leapt fiercely at the bandits, jumping up on his master's chest to protect him. The wrong-doers fled screaming in fear, never to return and in gratitude for his courage, the golden goddess awarded Sinh with her Sapphire blue eyes. To this day, Sinh's ancestors guard over the temple." Interestingly, the temple still stands and is populated by Siamese cats with striking blue eyes (typically, this breed has green eyes).

For hundreds of years, Blue Sapphires were the popular choice for engagement and wedding rings. Prince Charles expressed his love for Princess Diana with a Sapphire engagement ring.

Just the facts

The most desirable and expensive of the entire Sapphire family (with the exception of Padparadscha and more recently Pink Sapphire), Blue Sapphires come in a wide range of hues. Sapphires graduate in colour from light pastel blues all the way through to the depths of midnight blue. They are identical to Ruby (the red variety of corundum), except for one key component, their colour.

Sapphires that generate the highest value sit in the middle of the blue colour range, while the pale blues and darker midnight blues offer the best value.

Sapphires are one of the toughest gemstones, second in hardness only to Diamonds. They are mined from just beneath the Earth's surface or from alluvial deposits where they can be sifted out by hand.

Asterism or the star effect is a reflection effect that appears as two or more intersecting bands of light across the surface of a gem. This phenomenon is commonly found in Sapphires.

For full details of gemstone optical effects see page 153.

Dazzling Diamonds and 9k gold perfectly enhance this Sapphire

An urban inspired design containing 8 channel set Sapphires

This alluring ring contains 28 stunning Sapphires

SAPPHIRE

The mixture of cuts gives this pendant an individual sophistication

A rainbow of colours from Madagascar

14k white gold set with rich Blue Sapphires and sparkling Diamonds

Sapphire Locations

Gems TV sources its gems from various locations around the world. As the appearance of Sapphires varies slightly from each location, we have detailed some of our main sources below.

Ceylonese Sapphire

The island of Ceylon, known as Sri Lanka since 1972, holds the earliest records for the mining of Sapphires. Noted for their cornflower blues, Ceylonese Sapphires are synonymous with top quality and demand a premium in the gem world.

A classical source of quality Sapphires throughout history, mining occurs in the rich gem fields found beneath the tea-covered slopes of Elahera, Bibile and Rathnapura.

Ceylonese Sapphires received a boost in their popularity in 1981 when Prince Charles gave Lady Diana an engagement ring set with a stunning 18ct Ceylonese Sapphire.

Madagascan Sapphire

Madagascar provides some of the highest quality Sapphires and we are able to bring them to you at fantastic value.

Sapphires were first unearthed in the early 1990s. The Madagascan gem fields now account for approximately 20% of total global Sapphire production. The majority of Madagascar's Sapphires come from the prolific gem fields of Ilakaka and Antiermene.

Pailin Sapphire (Cambodia)

The Cambodian city of Pailin (the ancient Khmer word for "Blue Sapphire") is steeped in local folklore regarding its precious treasures: "Long ago when the men folk sharpened their spears to go out hunting, the gods feared for the local wildlife. The gods told the townsfolk to lay down their arms, explaining that if they promised not to hunt the beasts of the forests they would find something of far greater value in the streams

SAPPHIRE

and rivers. Sure enough, they found Sapphires in abundance."

Kanchanaburi Sapphire (Thailand)

The sleepy province of Kanchanaburi, renowned for the Bridge Over The River Kwai, rests amongst the jungle clad valleys of Western Thailand.

Kanchanaburi's Bo Ploi Sapphire mines were discovered in 1919, and today remain one of world's premier sources of Blue Sapphires. The Sapphires of Bo Ploi are mined from alluvial deposits spread over 320 hectares.The miners of Bo Ploi tell us that they must unearth over 50 tons of alluvial soil to extract just 1ct of Sapphire Crystal.

Sapphires have been mined from the Bo Ploi mines throughout the last ten years and they are approaching depletion. This increasing rarity makes these Sapphires a must for any jewellery collection.

Australian Sapphire (Australia)

Some of the finest Sapphires in the world herald from this sunburnt country. Top quality Australian Sapphires exhibit brilliant cornflower blues usually associated with those from Ceylon (Sri Lanka).

Sapphires have been mined in Australia for over 100 years, the majority come from three fields: the Anakie fields in Central Queensland, the Lava Plains in Northern Queensland and the New England fields around Inverell in the north east of New South Wales.

During the 1980's, Australia produced about 70% of the world's Sapphires and although production has decreased, the demand from the international market for Australian Sapphires remains very high.

Sapphires found in Australia originate from similar geographic conditions to those of Thailand and Cambodia, and have similar properties.

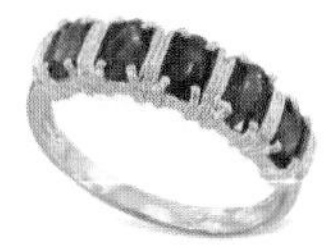

A simply elegant ring made up of 5 flawless Blue Sapphires

The woven design of this ring contains 29 channel set Sapphires

The brilliance of this Sapphire shines through when coupled with Diamonds and set in 18k gold

Here we have Sapphires from different corners of the globe creating this stunning two tone ring

SAPPHIRE

This regal looking ring contains a royal Blue Sapphire circled by 24 Diamonds

Simple beauty made up of 4 Sapphire gems

A traditional heart shape given an exotic twist with 41 square cut Sapphires

SAPPHIRE:	September's birthstone
Locations:	Madagascar, Tanzania, Nigeria, Australia, Cambodia, Thailand, Sri Lanka, Kenya
Colours Found:	Fancy
Typical Cuts:	All cuts
Family:	Corundum
Hardness:	9.00
Refractive Index:	1.76 - 1.77
Relative Density:	3.90 - 4.10

Nigerian Sapphire (Nigeria)

Nigeria plays a key role in supplying the world with some of the most popular gemstones. Nigerian Sapphire is mined at Nisama Jama'a in Nigeria's Kaduna State.

Umba River Sapphire (Tanzania)

On the Great North Road in Tanzania, between the plains of the Serengeti and the foothills of Mount Kilimanjaro lies Arusha, the gateway to the beating heart of Africa and home to the fabled gemstone mines of the Umba Valley.

Collecting in rich alluvial deposits that run the course of the valley, Umba River Sapphire is sourced using age-old mining techniques by Waarusha and Wameru miners whose knowledge of gemstones has been handed down for generations.

Chanthaburi Sapphire (Thailand)

Black Star Sapphire has only ever been found at one place on Earth - Chanthaburi. From these mines, no more than 7 kilometres from the Gems TV design and production facility, Blue, Green and Yellow Sapphires are also unearthed.

Commonly called Muang Chan, Chanthaburi is a coastal province, which has played an important role in the history of the nation, both before and during the Rattanakosin (Bangkok) Period. With a population of 480,000 Chanthaburi possesses a wealth of natural resources including gorgeous gems.

Chanthaburi is about 245 kilometres East of Bangkok and close to the border of Cambodia. It is said that some 80% of the worlds Rubies and Sapphires pass through Chanthaburi to be either traded, cut, prepared or set into jewellery on their way to market!

With Gems TV being the biggest jewellery employer in the Province, it is easy to understand why today we are possibly the largest supplier of gem set jewellery in the world.

SAPPHIRE *(FANCY)*

Since the dawn of time, Sapphires have captivated and mesmerised jewellery connoisseurs the world over. From hot pink to forest green, Sapphire's spectrum of colours is truly kaleidoscopic.

Fancy Sapphires get their unique colours from the iron, chrome, titanium and other trace metals present within the corundum.

White Sapphire

White Sapphire is a variety that has found new favour in recent times and is arguably Sapphire in its purest form. With none of the iron, chrome, titanium and other trace metals that give Fancy Sapphires their unique colours, White Sapphire is a popular alternative to Diamonds.

A unique blend of Purple and Yellow Sapphires

Pink Sapphire

Pink Sapphires share a colour border with Ruby, many Pink sapphires are so close to this boundary they are termed as "Hot Pink".

Fancy Sapphires that remain firmly within the colour realms of pink, range from pastel pink shades to more vivacious hot pinks. Pink Sapphires are often used in tandem with Blue Sapphires to make interesting alternatives to accent Diamonds displaying bright, colourful but harmonious contrasts within a single piece of jewellery. Due to its growing popularity during 2004 and 2005 the gem trade witnessed a 40% increase in the price of Pink Sapphires. However, due to Gems TV's huge gemstone buying power, we were very successful in reversing the price trend.

Midnight Blue Sapphire surrounded by a burst of colour

5 different colours of Sapphire create this exciting design

Purple Sapphire

Prized by collectors, Purple Sapphires can display rich purple-pink colours reminiscent of orchids. One word of warning, when we do manage to source Purple Sapphire, they don't stay on our shelves for very long and are quickly snapped up by collectors and jewellery connoisseurs alike.

SAPPHIRE *(FANCY)*

Yellow Sapphire

Ranging from pleasing butter-like colours to intensely beautiful canary yellows, Yellow Sapphires are not just beautiful, but are one of the most valuable of all yellow gemstones available.

Green Sapphire

Green Sapphires display a range of green hues, from colours reminiscent of olives through to wine bottle greens.

Star Sapphire

With their very bright and lustrous star formations, Star Sapphires have traditionally been the most popular of all star gemstones.

Glance at a Star Sapphire and you will see six or even twelve rayed stars silently gliding across the gemstone's surface. This wonderful gem has long been coveted for its beautiful and mysterious optical effects know as "asterism" (See page 153).

Black Star Sapphires are only found in the Ban Kha Ja mine in the Chanthaburi Province of Thailand.

Colour Change Sapphire

Colour Change Sapphires come from the gem gravels of Tanzania. They present gem lovers with an opportunity to own the rare and stunning colour change effect in a gem other than Alexandrite.

Delicate Yellow Sapphires set into 9k gold earrings

Colourful and fun jewellery containing 16 precious gemstones

An exciting oval cut colour change Sapphire accented with Diamonds

FANCY SAPPHIRE:	September's birthstone
Locations:	Madagascar, Tanzania, Kenya, Australia, Thailand, Sri Lanka
Colours Found:	Yellow, pink, purple, lavender, white, green, orange, bi-colour, tri-colour
Typical Cuts:	All cuts
Family:	Corundum
Hardness:	9.00
Refractive Index:	1.76 - 1.77
Relative Density:	3.90 - 4.10

What our Craftsmen say:

Miss Bang-on Lakhiri
- Gem Matcher

"There is nothing more satisfying in gem sorting than to work on a multi-coloured Sapphire bracelet. Even though the task of matching colours is simplified by the fact that they are all different, the skill in balancing all of the different colours and hues is a true art in itself."

SAPPHIRE (*PADPARADSCHA*)

While Sapphires have mesmerised jewellery connoisseurs since the dawn of time, there is one Sapphire variety that mesmerises above all others, the mysterious and coveted Padparadscha Sapphire.

Padparadscha Sapphire derives its name from its resemblance to the beautiful and famed pinkish orange red lotus flower known to the Sri Lankan people as "Padparadscha" or, getting botanical, "Nelumbo Nucifera Speciosa."

Just the facts

Padparadscha Sapphires must combine elements of yellow, pink, red and orange in one gem to rightly claim their Padparadscha title. Taking their name from the flower, Padparadscha Sapphires are so rare and beautiful that they are highly prized and valued by collectors and connoisseurs. Widely regarded as the most valuable of all Sapphires, prices can reach many thousands of dollars per carat.

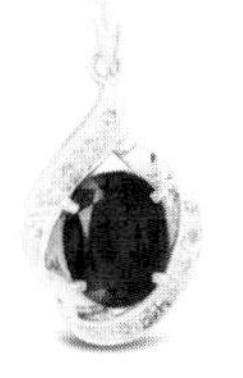

An 18k pendant of unquestionable beauty

Although sometimes you will hear people refer to Orange Sapphires as "Padparadscha like colour", unless they contain hues of yellow, pink and red, they are not the real thing. However, Orange Sapphires do offer a very beautiful natural alternative to this prized gem.

Simply the best

Deftly combining yellow, pink and red, with striking flashes of orange, in one tropical jewel, one way to picture the colour of Padparadscha Sapphires is to imagine sitting in front of a lazy fire on an isolated beach painted by the soothing hues of a tropical sunset. You then hold a fragrant lotus bloom to your nose and, at that instant, the colours blend creating an aurora of yellow, orange, red and pink. This is Padparadscha Sapphire.

Nothing quite compares to the stunning combination of white gold and Padparadscha Sapphire

Wonderfully romantic and delightfully seductive, Padparadscha Sapphires are so rare and beautiful that they are highly prized by collectors. But what are the origins of the word Padparadscha?

Often misunderstood, the modern word "Padparadscha" was adopted from a German gemological text early in the 20th Century.

Over 6ct of Padparadscha Sapphire - perfect, rare and beautiful

SAPPHIRE (*PADPARADSCHA*)

Some say that the word Padparadscha is actually a corruption of two Sanskrit and Singhalese words "Padma Raga". While "Padma" means lotus, the word "Raga" is more complex, meaning colour, attraction, desire and musical rhythm all in rolled into one!

Although the exact description is often debated, the beauty of these gemstones is not. While some continue to narrowly define Padparadscha as a Sri Lankan Sapphire, today, Padparadscha Sapphires are also recognised as hailing from Madagascar, Vietnam and Tanzania. Regardless of the locale, Padparadscha Sapphires, especially in larger sizes, are impossibly rare and historically sell at a huge premium.

Pear cut to perfection

With Gems TV's ability to acquire complete mining finds, in August 2005, we were able to secure one of the largest collections of Padparadscha Sapphires ever known. The quality of these gems are second to none and during the end of 2005 and early 2006, these extremely rare gems will be set into glorious jewellery. All collectors and gem fanatics should keep their eyes firmly peeled for their appearance, put simply – they are breathtaking.

Over 3ct of Padparadscha flanked by 6 Diamonds

Don't forget that, as with many of the rarer gemstones that we offer, there is never a guarantee of continuous supply. Padparadscha Sapphire certainly fits into this category and, prior to August 2005, we had only sold eleven pieces of jewellery featuring this gemstone in the previous six months!

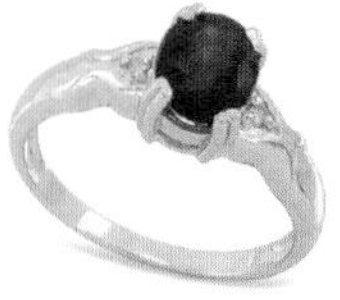

The explosion of colour of this Madagascan gem is unmatchable

PADPARADSCHA SAPPHIRE	
Locations:	Sri Lanka, Madagascar, Tanzania, Vietnam
Colours Found:	Combining yellow, pink, red, with striking flashes of orange
Typical Cuts:	Oval, round, pear
Family:	Corundum
Hardness:	9.00
Refractive Index:	1.76 - 1.77
Relative Density:	3.90 - 4.10

Don Kogen, the Gem Hunter says:

"A true Sapphire connoisseur's delight! When I manage to source Padparadscha Sapphire, don't hesitate to acquire it or you will be too late. With my contacts at the Madagascan gem fields of Ilakaka, when Mother Nature passes over her prized possession, I ensure my team of buyers are always first on hand"

SCAPOLITE

Scapolite was discovered in 1913 in the Mogok Stone Tract of upper Burma. Scapolite comes from the Greek words "Scapos", meaning rod and "Lithos", meaning stone. It gets its name from the stick or rod-like appearance of its crystals. Scapolite is also known as Wernerite for the German explorer and mineralogist Abraham Gottlob Werner (1750–1817).

Legends and lore

While Scapolite has virtually no specific legends or lore, its cat's eye variety has been attributed with some metaphysical attributes.

Wearing a high quality Cat's Eye Scapolite is believed by some to make one wealthy, healthy, strongly determined, knowledgeable and it also provides protection from enemies.

It is also believed to help one gain insight and psychic powers.

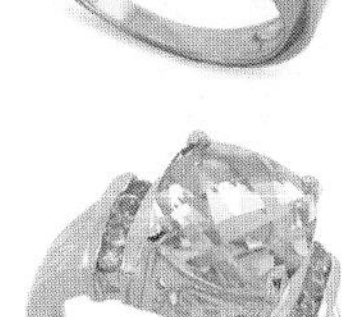

Flawlessly faceted Brazilian Scapolite stunningly set into 18k gold

A rare blend of Scapolite and Kornerupine

Just the facts

As Scapolite is a mixture of minerals, with varying specific gravity and refractive indexes, it can be easily confused with Amethyst, Citrine, Chrysoberyl and Golden Beryl. However, Scapolite can be differentiated from these other gems by the use of a long-wave ultra-violet light.

Scapolite fluoresces with a yellowish to orange colour, while Quartz and Beryl do not display such fluorescence.

Scapolite minerals are Silicates of Aluminium with Calcium and Sodium.

Scapolite is unusually found as prismatic crystals in metamorphic rocks and only very occasionally in igneous rocks.

While very attractive, Scapolite is not a well known gemstone and as Scapolite is not a common mineral, examples are very rare.

Scapolite only made a few appearances at Gems TV during 2005 and the word from our gem hunters is that it is unlikely to surface in any great quantity during 2006.

Ian Danter
Gems TV Presenter

"All items of jewellery shown in this guide were crafted by Gems TV during 2005 and were sold direct to the public. The average selling price was amazingly under £65!

During 2006 we anticipate introducing a further 22,700 individual designs, featuring approximately 490 different gem types."

SCAPOLITE:	Mixture of minerals
Locations:	Brazil, Madagascar, India, China, Sri Lanka, Kenya, Mozambique, Tanzania, Kenya, Canada
Colours Found:	Yellowish to orange
Typical Cuts:	All Cuts
Family:	Scapolite
Hardness:	5.50 - 6.00
Refractive Index:	1.54 - 6.00
Relative Density:	2.56 - 2.77

SILLIMANITE

An excellent example of the chatoyancy found in Sillimanite

Indian Sillimanite Cat's Eye set in 9k gold

A bezel set Sillimanite gem is used to produce this captivating pendant

SILLIMANITE:	Occurs in schists and gneisses
Locations:	Brazil, Sri Lanka, India, Czech Republic
Colours Found:	Colourless, white, brown, yellow, blue, green
Typical Cuts:	All cuts, ornamentals
Family:	Sillimantine
Hardness:	6.00 - 7.00
Refractive Index:	1.65 - 1.68
Relative Density:	3.24

Sillimanite derives its name from Benjamin Silliman (1779-1864), who was a famous American geologist. Sillimanite is sometime referred to as Fibrolite.

Legends and lore

As Sillimanite is an exotic gemstone, it has yet to attract any notable legends or folklore and given is extreme rarity, this is unlikely to change in the foreseeable future.

Just the facts

Pure specimens of Sillimanite are not terribly common. Typically it is found scattered within layers of metamorphic rocks which have been put under great pressure and high temperature. This is why Sillimanite is commonly found in volcanic or hot spring areas.

Sillimanite is a polymorph with two other minerals; Kyanite and Andalusite. A polymorph is a mineral that shares the same chemistry but a different crystal structure with another, or other, minerals.

This is a very rare gem and due to its brittleness is very difficult to cut. Some 50% can be wasted in the faceting and fashioning process.

Some Sillimanite crystals demonstrate chatoyancy (also known as the "cat's eye effect", this is caused by minerals reflecting a single band of light back to the eye), and make stunning cabochon rings and earrings.

Sillimanite is found in several locations worldwide including: Brazil, Central Europe, Myanmar, Sri Lanka, Czech Republic, India, Italy, Germany and Idaho in the United States. Sillimanite is formed from aluminium silicate (Al2SiO5) and is mostly found as silky, fibrous masses and (rarely) as transparent prismatic crystals with glassy lustre.

Because of the way it is scattered within the host rocks, miners often have difficulty in detecting Sillimanite making this gem exceedingly rare.

SODALITE

Sodalite is a rare, rich royal blue gemstone. Discovered in the early 1800's in Greenland, Sodalite was named because of its high sodium content. Sodalite is a member of the Sodalite group and, together with Hauyne, Nosean and Lazurite, is a component of Lapis Lazuli.

Sodalite, quite well known in the semi-precious gemstone trade, did not become important as a gemstone until 1891 when it was unearthed at a deposit near Bancroft, Ontario by Frank D. Adams while he was investigating the geology of the Haliburton-Hastings area for the Geological Survey of Canada.

Legends and lore

Sodalite has been named, "Princess Blue", after Princess Patricia who visited Ontario shortly after Sodalite's discovery in Canada. She subsequently selected Sodalite for the interior decoration of Marlborough House in England.

Sodalite is believed by some crystal healers to help clear up mental confusion and establish inner peace. Sodalite is also regarded as capable of strengthening the power of the mind over the body, by bridging the gap between thoughts and feelings.

Sodalite is believed by some to be an excellent gemstone for enhancing the communication skills of mediators and peace makers, and is credited as being good for healing rifts in partnerships and relationships, and helping to bring an end to arguments or disagreements.

Physically, Sodalite is attributed to opening the throat chakra.

Sodalite Hackmanite faceted to enhance its subtle green hues

A baguette cut Sodalite Hackmanite enhanced by the Diamond set above

By setting this Sodalite in sterling silver the eye is drawn to its distinctive mottled colouring

Just the facts

Sodalite is the main mineral of the Sodalite group which is composed of minerals with a similar isometric structure and related chemistry.

The Sodalite group is also a sub-group within a group. Its members are also part of a larger group called the Feldspathoids (similar to Feldspars but with less silica content), which are low-silica igneous minerals.

SODALITE

Drew Nicholls
Gems TV Presenter

"All items of jewellery shown in this guide were crafted by Gems TV during 2005 and were sold direct to the public. The average selling price was amazingly under £65!

During 2006 we anticipate introducing a further 22,700 individual designs, featuring approximately 490 different gem types."

SODALITE:	Vitreous, transparent to translucent crystals
Locations:	Namibia, South Africa, Brazil, Canada, U.S.A, Brazil, Bolivia, Ecuador, Greenland, Italy, Romania, Russia, Australia, Germany
Colours Found:	Grey, yellow, green or pink with white veins or patches
Typical Cuts:	Fancy, cabochon
Family:	Sodalite and Feldspathoids
Hardness:	5.00 - 6.00
Refractive Index:	1.48
Relative Density:	2.10 - 2.30

Sodalite crystals are vitreous and transparent to translucent, however, large specimens can appear opaque.

Although Sodalite appears similar to Lapis Lazuli, Sodalite is a royal blue rather than ultramarine and rarely contains Pyrite, a common inclusion in Lapis.

It is further distinguished from similar minerals by its white streak of Calcite. Sodalite's six directions of cleavage may be seen as incipient cracks running through the gemstone.

Clear crystals are very rare and are hardly ever large enough to be faceted. Most specimens are massive and these are polished into ornamental slabs, inlays, carvings, spheres, eggs, beads and cabochons.

Well known for its blue colour, Sodalite may also be grey, yellow, green or pink and is often mottled with white veins or patches.

There are two main varieties of Sodalite: One called Hackmanite, which contains a higher concentration of sodium than the basic form, and one called Molybdosodalite, which contains less chlorine than the basic form.

A new variety of Sodalite found in Greenland is the green specimen nicknamed "Chameleon Sodalite".

The world's most important deposits of Sodalite are in Canada, U.S.A, Brazil, Bolivia, Ecuador, Greenland, Italy, Romania, Russia, Australia, Germany, Namibia and South Africa.

What our Craftsmen say:
Miss Bang-on Lakhiri - Quality Assurance

"Sodalite is definitely a gem with a fascinating split personality and as a result, at the workshop, we take two different approaches.

The larger opaque varieties are typically crafted into silver necklaces and bracelets, while rarer, more transparent Sodalite is faceted and handcrafted into gold jewellery"

SPHENE

Sphene is named after the Greek word for wedge, because of its typical wedge shaped crystal. As it contains titanium, Sphene is also sometimes referred to as Titanite.

One of the world's newest and rarest gems, Sphene has a rather unusual ability to take a beam of light and break it into all of the spectral colours. This combined with its strong pleochroism has the effect of making the gem appear to change colour depending on which angle you are looking at it from. Occasionally pink, black or brown, most Sphene is predominantly green or yellowish-green, with just about every other colour of the rainbow mixed in somewhere.

Just the facts

Sphene makes gorgeously brilliant, fiery gems that have a higher dispersion (i.e. fire) than Diamonds.

Sphene's magnificent fire, unique colour shades, strong pleochroism, adamantine (i.e. Diamond-like) lustre and double refraction (i.e. birefringence) make it ideal for earrings and pendants that catch the light and show its sparkling qualities.

The high birefringence usually makes some doubling of facet images visible within the gem giving it a degree of internal "fuzziness" similar to that often seen in Zircon. Clean gems larger than a few carats are extremely rare.

Sphene is found in a variety of locations worldwide including Mexico, Brazil, Canada, U.S.A, Sri Lanka, Madagascar, Switzerland, Italy, Pakistan and Russia.

An oval cabochon cut Sphene in a traditional four prong setting

Flawless faceting enhances the internal fire of these Sphene earrings

A simplistic yet elegant pendant containing a bezel set Brazilian Sphene

Don Kogen, the Gem Hunter says:

"Ignore the name its got more fire than Diamonds! Sphene is one of my favourite gems. It's got beauty, it's got rarity and because of the way I can source it, we make it affordable too!"

SPHENE: Can break a beam of light into all spectral colours	
Locations:	Madagascar, Brazil, Pakistan, Sri Lanka, Mexico, Canada, U.S.A, Switzerland, Italy, Russia
Colours Found:	Pink, black or brown, green or yellowish-green
Typical Cuts:	All cuts
Family:	Sphene
Hardness:	5.50
Refractive Index:	1.885 - 2.05
Relative Density:	3.40 - 3.56

SPINEL

Spinel was first recognised as a separate gem species in 1587. Spinel's name is either derived from the Latin word for thorn "Spina", as a result of its characteristic octahedral crystals having pointed ends, or from the Greek word for spark "Spintharis", in reference to the gem's bright red hues.

Spinel was once mistaken for Ruby, but it's no imposter, rather a "Master of Disguise". One of the Gem Kingdom's best-kept secrets, Spinel is treasured for its eternal brilliance and spectacular colours. Whether your fascination with gems is for their beauty, rarity or history, Spinel is a superb addition to your jewellery collection.

A perfect example of 9k white gold used to enhance the natural lustre of this gem

Legends and lore

Because of its mistaken identity, Spinel has few historical references. However, Spinels have a bizarre association with sorcerers and alchemists. Spinels were used by practitioners of the "Dark Arts" to summon demons and were also used as amulets to protect them from fire.

Oval cut Spinel in a contemporary bar setting perfectly complemented by channel set Garnets

Spinels occupy a unique place in gemstone history. Up until the 19th Century, the intense colouration displayed by Noble Red Spinel led some to mistakenly identify this gem as Ruby. The source of confusion stemmed not only from colour similarities, but also the close proximity of their deposits.

A blend of Spinel, Tanzanite and Green Diamonds create this attractive design

Noble Red Spinel's near-identical resemblance to Ruby led to it being a prodigious, albeit accidental feature in many of the world's most famous gem collections, including the Vatican's and the Crown Jewels of Russia, Iran and England. Interestingly, both the legendary 352ct "Timur Ruby" and the 170ct "Black Prince's Ruby" that feature in British Imperial State Crowns proved to be Noble Red Spinels!

The cushion cut of this Spinel emphasises the inner fire of this gem

In 1415, at the "Battle of Agincourt", the English King, Henry V, wore a helmet garnished with jewels including the "Black Prince's Ruby". During the battle, the French commander, the Duke Of Alenon, struck Henry's head a mighty

blow with his battle-axe, nearly killing the king. Surprisingly, the force of the blow glanced off the Spinel saving his life, allowing Henry to lead his troops to what many thought would be an impossible victory.

Just the facts

Spinels occur in many colours: reds, blues, pinks, oranges and other "Fancy Colours". Apart from specific colours, Spinel's names include:

Almandine Spinel

The violet variety of Spinel, Almandine is very hard to find and looks magnificent when set in rings.

Balas Ruby

The common historical name for Spinel, which referred to their country of origin, either Badakshan in Tajikistan or the Balaksh region of Sri Lanka.

Cobalt Spinel

Resembling fine Sapphires, these exceptional Blue Spinels from Sri Lanka are coloured by cobalt.

Flame Spinel

The orange-red variety of Spinel, with a glorious fire, this gem works best when set in white gold.

Gahnite or Gahnospinel

Named after Swedish chemist L. G. Gahn, it is the rare greenish or bluish, zinc-rich variety of Spinel.

Noble Red Spinel

Ruby-red variety of Spinel. Believed by many in history to be a ruby, this master of disguise is even set into the crown jewels.

Rubicelle

Yellow to orange variety of Spinel.

The reality behind Noble Red Spinel's Ruby-like appearance is due to it being found in close proximity to corundum, the base mineral of Rubies and Sapphires, and Chromium, the Midas element responsible for giving both Noble Red Spinels and Rubies their deep red colour.

A modern design featuring a 9k white gold bar setting

6 round cut Spinel gems are incorporated in this unique pendant

A beautiful combination of Spinel and Tourmaline

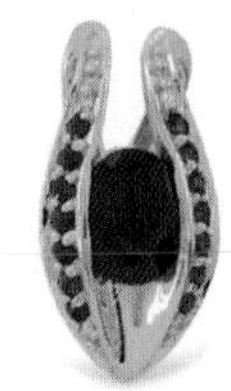

The deep red of this Spinel is balanced by the Padparadscha Sapphires running down each side

SPINEL

Today, Spinels can be easily identified by their refractivity. Since Noble Red Spinels are singly refractive and Rubies doubly refractive, the primary colour in Noble Red Spinels appears purer and more intense than the reds seen in many Rubies.

Spinels are mined from alluvial deposits or directly from large granular granite or other igneous host rocks. Spinels come from a handful of sources including Madagascar, the Mahenge region of South Central Tanzania, Tundura on Tanzania's remote South East and Central Vietnam's Luc Yen region. Perfect octahedral crystals are sometimes set into jewellery in their original uncut octahedral states. The Burmese refer to these gems as "nat thwe", meaning "spirit polished". Sometimes "nat thwe" Spinels will receive a very light polishing.

12 channel set Garnets draw the eye to the 1.1ct Cambodian Spinel

Pure Spinel is white, but impurities give it a wide range of colours. Almost all colours are used in jewellery, but the most valuable and popular colour is Noble Red Spinel. Occasionally, colour change varieties are found, turning colour from a light grey blue in daylight to a light purple under candlelight.

Even when combined with other stunning gems the natural beauty of Spinel still dominates

Even though they are more affordable, did you know that Spinels are rarer than Rubies? In the Gem Kingdom, "rare" can be both a blessing and a curse, as this affects market prices and availability. This is unfortunate for the Spinel miner, but great news for everyone else as they are one of nature's most beautiful treasures.

Spinels are intensely coloured without any secondary tones. Their high refractive index makes cutting very important - the brilliance of a well-cut Spinel is breathtaking.

SPINEL:	Intense colouration
Locations:	Madagascar, Vietnam, Tanzania, Sri Lanka
Colours Found:	Fancy
Typical Cuts:	All cuts
Family:	Spinel
Hardness:	8.00
Refractive Index:	1.715 - 1.720
Relative Density:	3.60

What our Craftsmen say:

Mr.Chalouy Bunthuen - Gem setting

"As Spinels are extremely durable, we often set them in very minimal prong settings, to allow the maximum amount of the gem to be displayed. If the rough is of ample size, we will often try and fashion it into a cushion cut."

SUNSTONE

Radiating with the power of eternal light, Sunstone has been coveted since antiquity for its ability to guide its wearer through the journey of life. It is also known as Aventurine Feldspar or Heliolite from the Greek "helios" for sun and "lithos" for stone.

Legends and lore

An ancient gem, Sunstone has been discovered in Viking Burial mounds. Among the Vikings, Sunstone was thought to aid navigation both in reality and during one's journey to Valhalla and the afterlife.

Pope Clement VII (1478-1534) was reputed to have in his possession a Sunstone with a golden spot that moved across the surface in accordance with the apparent motion of the sun from sunrise to sunset.

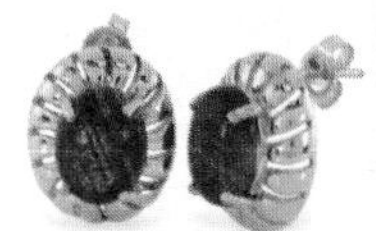

Set in 9k gold these Indian Sunstones demonstrate the natural 'schiller' of this gem

The Native Americans in Oregon used Sunstone for trade and barter. Oregon Sunstone was declared the official Gemstone of the State of Oregon in 1987.

Crystal healers believe Sunstone to be useful for adding personal insight and alleviating depression and its colours will put sweetness back into your life.

This impressive piece contains a 9.6ct baguette cut Sunstone coupled with 10 pave set Yellow Diamonds

They also believe that it is a cleansing gem useful for clearing all the Chakras.

Historically, Sunstone has been linked with benevolent gods, luck and good fortune.

Sunstone is said by some to act as an antidepressant that helps lift dark moods. It is also said to remove thoughts discrimination and abandonment.

This remarkable design contains an oval cabochon cut Sunstone

Sunstone is further believed to reverse feelings of failure and to increase confidence.

Because Sunstone is alchemical gem, it is said to have a profound connection to light and is believed to possess the power to harnesses the regenerated power of the sun during every day life.

An elegant cabochon Sunstone set in a 9k gold pendant

SUNSTONE

A regal gem set into a regal design

Rich orange hues and deep red tones give this Sunstone bracelet an exotic flair

SUNSTONE:	State gem of Oregon
Locations:	Madagascar, India, U. S. A
Colours Found:	Water clear, pale yellow, soft pink, claret red to deep blue and green
Typical Cuts:	All cuts
Family:	Feldspar
Hardness:	6.00 - 6.50
Refractive Index:	1.53 - 1.55
Relative Density:	2.62 - 2.65

Just the facts

Sunstone is a member of the Feldspar group of minerals and is closely related to Moonstone. The name Feldspar comes from the German "Feldt Spat", meaning "Field Stone". This is because, when Feldspar weathers, it releases large amounts of plant nutrients, such as potassium, which enrich the soil.

Sunstone has a beautiful, glittering, sunlight effect, as a result of its tiny metallic inclusions. The copper or pyrite inclusions cause sparkling flashes of light as millions of particles playfully interact with light. This feature is known as "Schiller" or "Aventurescence". Sunstones are nearly always cut as cabochons to reflect this phenomenon, but the deeper colours may also be faceted to exhibit their superior lustre.

Sunstone is formed and crystallised in lava flows. Sunstones range in colour from water clear through pale yellow, soft pink, and claret red to deep blue and green. Some of the deeper coloured gems have bands of varying colour while others exhibit pleochroism, showing two different colours when viewed from different directions.

Sunstones are mined from the surface from partially decomposed rock with a pick and shovel or from shallow pits dug to retrieve the rough.

Sunstone is mined in the U.S.A. (Warner Valley, Oregon - the high copper content of these "Oregon Sunstones" gives them their unique bright red orange colours), India (Tamil Nadu), Canada, Madagascar, Norway (Tvedstrand) and Russia (Lake Baikal). Interestingly, some Sunstones from Madagascar display asterism (also known as the "star effect", this is caused by minerals reflecting a star of light back to the eye), which further accentuates Sunstone's natural sparkle.

TANOLITE™

As far back as AD 77, Pliny the Elder in his "Historis Naturalis" cited India as a major source of the world's most coveted gemstones. Today, India continues this tradition with our discovery of Tanolite™, a stunning new variety of Iolite trademarked by Gems TV.

Just the facts

Nestled in the Bay of Bengal, two thirds of the Indian State of Orissa is covered with Pre-Cambrian rocks that have long been known to include many gemstones. Orissa yields a plethora of coloured gemstones including Ruby, Sapphire, Aquamarine, Garnet, Topaz, Zircon, Tourmaline and of course, Iolite. By virtue of their colour, transparency, size, brilliance and flawlessness, Orissa's gemstones are known the world over.

It is in Orissa, with its tradition of gemstone excellence, that we recently unearthed new deposits of Iolite (see page 61). And herein lay the problem; this Iolite was nothing like anything we had ever seen before. Sporting beautiful violet hues, on a cursory glance, more than one of our buyers would muffle, "Is this Tanzanite?" Knowing better, Don "The Gem Hunter" would crack a smile before revealing its Indian lineage. But this also gave him an idea. He had discovered this gem, so why not trademark a special name? In homage to its visual similarities with Tanzanite, a new gem was born.

The Tanolite™ used in this adorable design proved a very popular choice

Tanolite™ is mined in the metamorphic rocks of Orissa's Kalahandi and Nawapada Districts. It occurs as large, transparent violet crystals with excellent lustre and brilliance. While Iolite is known as "Water Sapphire" due to its similar appearance to light blue Sapphire, Tanolite™ is a wonderfully affordable alternative to one of the world's most popular gems, Tanzanite. Jokingly referred to as "Water Tanzanite" by our gem sorters, its similarity to Tanzanite is not just skin deep. Both Tanzanite and Tanolite™ are strongly pleochroic, meaning they show many colours in a single gem depending on the viewing angle.

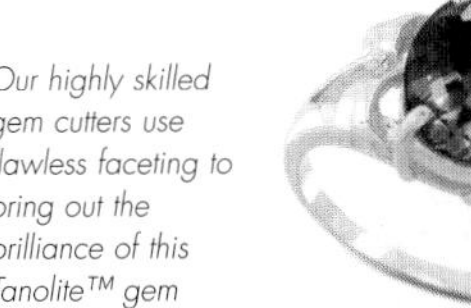

Our highly skilled gem cutters use flawless faceting to bring out the brilliance of this Tanolite™ gem

Amazingly precise hand faceting gives this gem star quality

TANOLITE™

The only place you will ever obtain Tanolite™ is on Gems TV.

In the UK watch us 24 hours a day on: Sky Guide 646 and NTL 177

1.5ct of Tanolite™ in a perfectly balanced white gold setting

A 3ct Indian Tanolite™, perfectly faceted and set on 18k white gold

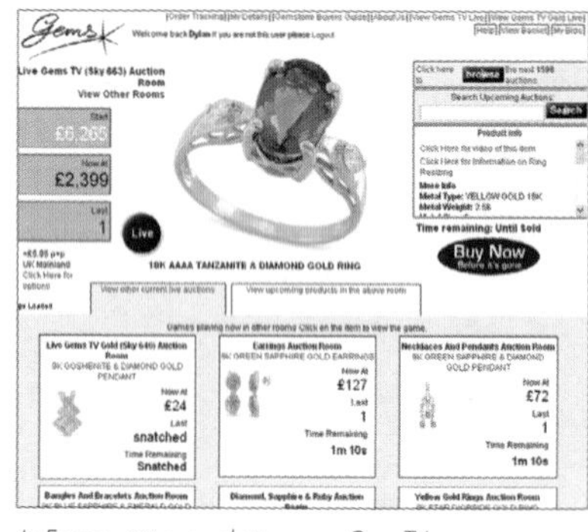

In Europe visit our website: www.GemsTV.com

TANOLITE™:	Pleochorism
Locations:	India
Colours Found:	Change colour from royal blue to deep purple
Typical Cuts:	All cuts
Family:	Cordierite
Hardness:	7.00 - 7.50
Refractive Index:	1.50
Relative Density:	2.53 - 2.65

In America and Asia visit our website: www.Thaigem.com

TANZANITE

Demand for Tanzanite has rocketed in recent years, outstripping sales of all other precious gems, with the exception of Sapphire. A thousand times rarer than Diamonds and with a little over a decade of mine life remaining, Tanzanite is the fashion gem of the Millennium.

Legends and lore

The romance of Tanzanite begins in the arid Merelani foothills of Mount Kilimanjaro. Born of fire, Tanzanite's beauty remained secret to Tanzania's nomadic Massai until 1967. Legend has it that a short lived grass fire caused by a lightning strike was the first catalyst that turned brown surface pebbles of Zoisite (Tanzanite's gemological name) into the vibrant blues spotted by Massai herdsmen. While wonderfully romantic, it is now generally regarded as unlikely that enough heat could be generated by such a fire to affect such a transformation.

This intricate design contains 13 hand set Tanzanite gems

Tanzanite soon found its way to America, arriving at the New York based jewellers Tiffany & Co. Louis Comfort Tiffany was immediately enraptured by it's beauty but disturbed by its gemological name of "Blue Zoisite", that to him echoed "Blue Suicide". As with anything in fashion, it's all in the name, and so this rare and exotic African gemstone was christened Tanzanite.

The channel setting in this gentlemen's ring holds the Tanzanite gems securely in place

Tanzanite's blue-purple fire soon took the fashion world by storm and was heralded "The Gemstone of the 20th Century". Demand for Tanzanite jewellery grew dramatically as its global appreciation increased and, in 1998 and 1999, Tanzanite was proclaimed the world's best selling gemstone.

Expert faceting brings out the lustre in this unusual Paraiba colour Tanzanite

Tanzanite continues to be all the rage in contemporary jewellery. Tom Ford, of the Paris and Milan fashion house Gucci, has dominated the catwalks with a collection modelling exotic blue gems, including Tanzanite.

At the 2004 Oscars, Eileen Penn, mother of Oscar winner Sean Penn, stole the limelight from her son in a stunning Tanzanite and Diamond cross pendant.

A balance of Tanzanite, Aquamarine and Tourmaline in an exquisite bracelet

TANZANITE

Just the facts

A key ingredient in Tanzanite's success is that it exhibits more shades of blue than a clear midnight sky due to a phenomenon called "pleochroism", whereby different colours are seen in different directions of the gemstone. When you look at Tanzanite in daylight, it sparkles a vibrant royal blue, but under candlelight luxuriant deep purples exude. Most of the time, you can actually see both colours simultaneously; this is especially true in larger carat sizes where Tanzanite's sparkling fire intensifies.

Although traditionally thought of as an intensely purple-blue gemstone, Tanzanite also occurs in a variety of other colours such as pink, green, ultramarine and a steely kind of blue. Frequently these Tanzanites exhibit a colour change from the more bluish hues under daylight, to pinkish violets under incandescent light.

A rare Green Tanzanite in a contemporary prong set pendant

Tanzanite is also coveted because of its rarity. Tanzanite's production is slowly but surely decreasing and many experts are of the opinion that Tanzanite will disappear in years to come. This has led to Tanzanite gaining considerable value; after all, the desire to own something unique has always been a decisive factor in fashion.

A modern yet timeless design featuring 5 Green Tanzanites

Tanzanite typically starts life as greenish brown Zoisite that is heated to 600 degrees Celsius to reveal its vibrant violet blue colours.

However, unlike regular Tanzanite, Coloured Tanzanite is the product of an extremely rare phenomenon, where the heat and pressure of underground water filled caves naturally changes the brown crystal into highly coveted natural colours. In gemology, the technically correct name for these gems is "(Colour Prefix) Zoisite"; however Coloured Tanzanite is generally accepted in the marketplace due to the gem's popularity.

AAAA Tanzanite trilliant cut to enhance the inner fire

Pink Tanzanite

This gem has it all. All the value and rarity of Tanzanite, but in a colour that is every girl's favourite. It is very seldom seen, it is normally

TANZANITE

snapped up by jewellery fanatics before we even have the chance to put them in their presentation boxes.

Green Tanzanite

You have to see this gem to believe it. Its colour and hues are truly magnificent.

Bi Colour Tanzanite

A gem that will confuse everyone and have your friends guessing for hours. Not only is it extremely rare, it is staggeringly beautiful.

Ultramarine Tanzanite

As the name suggests, this is a very light blue Tanzanite and is perfect for Aquamarine fans who want a gem similar in colour, but far more exclusive.

Floral heaven! Over 4ct of Tanzanite cut to delight

Tanzanite mining

As Tanzanite is exclusively mined in East Africa, in an area of Tanzania known as Merelani, we felt it was an appropriate opportunity to explain this one mining region in great detail.

Stunning AAAA Tanzanite beautifully enhanced by the 18k white gold setting

The Tanzanite deposits are hosted in metamorphic rocks, marbles and schists that belong to the Mozambique Belt (Rift Valley). The deposits run through the low hills of Merelani that rise from the hot Sanya plains, close to Mount Kilimanjiro.

Running at an angle of 41 degrees from the bowels of the Earth to the surface, the deposit line or horizon periodically folds over itself creating richly concentrated pockets of Tanzanite. These pockets provide gem miners with the richest pickings of these coveted green, pink, ultramarine and purple-blue gemstones.

2.3ct of antique cut AAAA Tanzanite

The Tanzanite mining area has been divided into four different sections known as "Blocks", respectively lettered A, B, C and D.

The different blocks together barely cover 20 square kilometres and have been parcelled out to different mining groups.

A contemporary bezel setting and 26 Diamonds made this AAAA Tanzanite ring award winning

TANZANITE

Although AAA colours come from all blocks, the "D Block" subsection has earned the reputation and kudos for producing the very rare and very beautiful "AAA" quality Tanzanite (only 1% of Tanzanite mined is AAA quality). Characterised by intensely deep purples with glistening flashes of red, the finest D Block Tanzanite can be likened to an old French wine of an impossibly hard to get hold of vintage. Many jewellers will not have been fortunate enough to see D Block AAA Tanzanite, as the vast majority of higher quality Tanzanite on the market comes from the neighbouring C Block.

Rather than referring to the ultimate Tanzanite as "AAA" from D block, which sounds a very unromantic way to describe the most romantic of gemstones, Gems TV refers to AAA Tanzanite from D Block as "AAAA".

The largest scale and most sophisticated techniques used in Tanzanite mining and recovery take place in C Block. According to recent reports on C Block mining, there are three main shafts leading down from the surface, known as "Main", "Bravo" and "Delta". The "Main" shaft, located in the

This striking design contains 8 marquise cut Tanzanite surrounding the brilliant cut centre piece

An arresting pendant made entirely of Tanzanite and 9k gold

Sophisticated grace in this traditional design

Gavin "Gemstone Gav" Linsell says:

"On a recent visit to Merelani in Tanzania, just outside the gem trading town of Arusha, I was fortunate to experience Tanzanite mining first hand. Apart from the hustle and bustle of a gem mine, one of the reasons I love visiting gem locales around the globe is to gleam local knowledge.

I find gem folklore especially fascinating and one legend surrounding Tanzanite that intrigues me is how grass fires caused by lightning strikes were attributed to its first discovery. While grass fires would be unlikely to generate the heat necessary to reveal Tanzanite's beauty, I was surprised to learn from miners that this story may have originated from the practice of placing Tanzanite rough in grass huts that were then burnt. To this day, Massai artisanal miners use slow burning camp fires to effect Tanzanite's miraculous transformation. Regardless, Tanzanite is a mesmerising gem and much like Kashmiri Sapphire, in my generation it will most likely become a gem of the past."

middle of the Block, is planned to go some 400m in length along the 41 degree incline and will reach a vertical depth of 275m. "Bravo", situated towards the southern boundary of the Block, will be 300m in length and will reach a vertical depth of 200m, as will "Delta", which is located toward the northern boundary of the Block. An interceptor shaft, known the "JW", cuts the "Main" at a vertical depth of 200m. "JW" has produced the highest per ton yields found so far at an amazing 60ct per ton!

The four shafts of C Block provide corridors for access by personnel, the starting points of the mining "stations" and the haulage of Tanzanite ore to the surface by railway carts. The mining stations are the chambers and sub-shafts off the larger access shafts, which follow and exploit the richly concentrated folds of Tanzanite ore. The per ton yields for raw Tanzanite ore in C Block averages 22ct (about 4 grams) per processed ton!

Tanzanite exudes sophistication; it's the quintessence of class and at the same time communicates individuality and self-confidence. Lavish Tanzanite jewellery is suited to all ages, emphasising the non-conformity of the young and the sophistication of the mature. Tanzanite's wonderful colours, clarity and range of imaginative cuts lend themselves to prominent display. Fashionable drop-earrings and pendants accentuate Tanzanite to the fullest, but Tanzanite is most popularly featured as large carat sized solitaires mounted into prominent ring settings, showing off its scintillating colours to full effect.

Caroline Lyndsay
Gems TV Presenter

"All items of jewellery shown in this guide were crafted by Gems TV during 2005 and were sold direct to the public. The average selling price was amazingly under £65!

During 2006 we anticipate introducing a further 22,700 individual designs, featuring approximately 490 different gem types."

TANZANITE *(AAAA)*

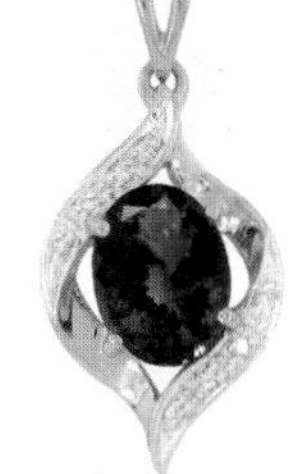

An elegant 18k pendant surrounded by quality accent Diamonds

A beautiful one of a kind AAAA Tanzanite

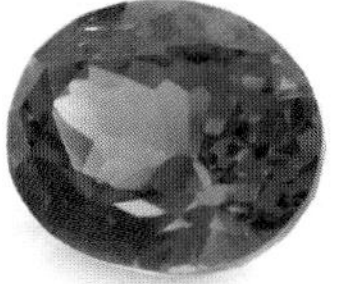

TANZANITE:	December's birthstone
Locations:	Tanzania
Colours Found:	Change colour from royal blue to deep purple
Typical Cuts:	Oval, octagon, cushion
Family:	Zoisite
Hardness:	6.50 - 7.00
Refractive Index:	1.68 - 1.72
Relative Density:	3.35

TEKTITE *(MOLDAVITE)*

Tektite comes from the Greek word "Tektos" meaning "Molten." It was the name given by Edward Suess who was born in London in 1831. He was a highly reputed professor at the University of Vienna, a geologist and a politician in the Austrian government.

A meteor is a small particle from space that appears as a bright light that completely burns up before it hits the ground: however, a Meteorite is a meteor that is large enough to reach the ground, without burning up completely.

Frequently exploding on impact, throwing pieces of rare and highly sought after Meteorite debris over a large area, these incredibly rare and collectable stones are the perfect gift for any keen collector of jewellery.

12 Aquamarine gems enclose the central Moldavite

Legends and lore

Collectively known as Tektites, they are normally assigned specific names based on their location. For example, Moldavites, named after the river Moldu in the Czech Republic, are found in this country as well as Austria and Germany, Australites are from Australia, Philippinites are from the Philippines and Southern China, Malaysianites are from Malaysia and Indochinites are from Thailand, Myanmar, China, Laos and Vietnam.

Perfectly matched Czech Moldavite set in 18k gold

Just the facts

Considered to be gemstones from space, Tektites are fragments of glass that are formed from Meteorite impacts with our planet.

This elegant pendant contains an octagon cut Moldavite with amazing lustre

Scientists believe that the Tektite's origin is the result of meteorite impact on either terrestrial or lunar rocks. The Tektites then formed when molten rock, created by the Meteorite's hyper-velocity impact, flew through the air, hardening into natural glass with aerodynamic forms and surface features.

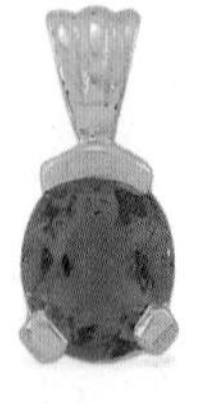

Eye-catchingly stylish Moldavite discovered in the Czech Republic

Some Tektites are smooth but others have rough, strongly eroded surfaces. Most Tektites are jet black but the Moldavites are dark to bottle green and are most suitable for faceting.

Tektite glass looks similar to Obsidian glass, which is a result of volcanic lava coming in contact with water, but can be differentiated by colour and chemical composition.

Tektites and associated impact melted rock are found in only a few regions on Earth (called Tektite strewn fields) and are, in most cases, associated with young impact craters on or near land.

Tektites come in two forms. The more common "Splash Form" Tektites have rounded aerodynamic shapes such as spheres, tear-drops, dumbbells and disks when they are well-preserved.

The second variety called "Layered" Tektites are found only in Southeast Asia. They have blocky, fragmental shapes and commonly display compositional layering and variations in bubble content. Some larger pieces have a surface reminiscent of lava or "Bread Crust" lava bombs.

There are far fewer Tektite localities on Earth than there are impact craters. This is because Tektites, being made entirely of glass, dissolve slowly with time. Therefore, Tektites are only preserved in abundance from large young impact events.

With approximately 650,000 Tektites ever collected, these gems from space are extremely rare and highly collectable. Considering that around 500,000 of these are Philippinites, Moldavites and Indochinites are true collectors' gems!

Our Tektite jewellery

We are not alone! Since the beginning of time the curiosity of humankind has been aroused by the descent of "shooting stars" or Meteorites into our world. So catch a falling star and discover the mystery behind this extraterrestrial gemstone in our wonderful range of tektite jewellery.

TEKTITE *(MOLDAVITE)*

Our designer's concept was to create an out of space design for an out of space gem

Another example of faultless faceting enhancing a gem's natural lustre

The green tones in this Czech Modavite is brilliantly balanced with the Green Tanzanite

TEKTITE:	Extraterrestrial gem
Locations:	Czech Republic, Austria, Germany, Australia, Philippines, China, Malaysia, Thailand, Myanmar, Laos, Vietnam
Colours Found:	Jet black
Typical Cuts:	Round, cabochon
Family:	Tektite
Hardness:	5.50 - 6.50
Refractive Index:	1.48 - 1.50
Relative Density:	5.50 - 6.50

TIGER'S EYE

Tiger's Eye is the best known variety of Chatoyant Quartz (or Cat's Eye Quartz). Tiger's Eye, with its bands resembling an eye of tiger, received its name due to this similarity. Tiger's Eye is also called Crocidolite Cat's Eye or African Cat's Eye. Tiger's Eye has rich yellow and golden brown stripes, with a fine golden lustre when polished.

Legends and lore

Many legends say that wearing Tiger's Eye is beneficial for health and spiritual well being. Legend also says it is a psychic protector, great for business and an aid to achieving clarity.

Coveted since antiquity, Roman soldiers wore Tiger's Eye for protection in battle. Due to its appearance, in the ancient world, Tiger's Eye was thought to be all seeing, offering protection during travel and strengthening convictions and confidence.

Today, crystal healers use Tiger's Eye for focusing the mind.

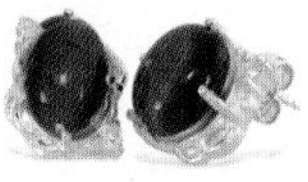

These 925 sterling silver earrings contain two 3.8ct golden Tiger's Eye gems

Simple elegance displaying the chatoyancy revealed in this magnificent Tiger's Eye

Just the facts

Tiger's Eye, a pseudomorph (i.e. the result of one mineral replacing another), is Quartz that contains oriented fibres of Crocidolite that have been replaced by Silica.

Tiger's Eye displays chatoyancy (a vertical luminescent band like that of a cat's eye). Tiger's Eye typically has lustrous alternating yellow or brown bands.

Cutting is crucial with Tiger's Eye because the rough gems reveal little or nothing of the exciting chatoyancy of the final cut and polished gems.

TIGER'S EYE:	Chatoyancy
Locations:	Namibia, South Africa, India, Brazil, Australia
Colours Found:	Rich yellow & golden brown stripes
Typical Cuts:	Cabochons
Family:	Quartz
Hardness:	7.00
Refractive Index:	1.55
Relative Density:	2.65

Other varieties of gems that can show chatoyancy (see page 154), include Alexandrite (page 9), Tourmaline (page 128) and Beryl (page 23). These gems however are not described as simply "Tiger's Eye" or "Cat's Eye", but are always prefixed by their gem variety.

TOPAZ

The origin of the name Topaz stirs confusion. Some references point to the Sanskrit word "Tapas", which means, "Fire". Some believe it is named after Zebirget, an island in the Red Sea that the Greeks once called Tapazius.

Topaz is an inherently romantic gem, and features regularly in the titles of romance novels and honeymoon destinations. Its name indicates beauty, rarity and wealth and imparts a sense of timelessness.

While the golden yellow and blues of Topaz are the most widely known, Topaz actually comes in a diverse array of striking colours. This when combined with its beauty, durability and surprising affordability, makes Topaz jewellery ideal for all occasions.

During 2005, Pink Topaz and Mystic Topaz were hugely popular on Gems TV and we expect to see increased demand for these lesser known Topaz varieties in 2006.

A magnificent 12.2ct Swiss Blue Topaz

Legends and lore

Many ancient traditions and beliefs have created a brilliant history for Topaz. The Egyptians called Topaz the "Gem Of The Sun", believing it was coloured by the golden glow of their sun god Ra and was thus a powerful protector from harm.

A modern triple prong setting holds these hand cut pear shaped Topaz

Greeks and Romans also associated the golden crystals with their Sun God, Jupiter. They believed the gem increased their strength and could neutralise enchantments.

An effortlessly stunning design featuring 12 2ct Topaz

Bushmen in Africa used Topaz in healing ceremonies and rituals to connect with ancestral spirits.

In medieval courts, Kings, judges and other noble persons were often presented with an engraved Topaz to win favour and cultivate positive relationships.

At the height of Imperial Russia's power, rich orange-pink Topaz gems were brought from Brazil to decorate the jewellery of the Czarinas. Ever since, these colours have been known as Imperial Topaz and even today, remain one of the most sought after varieties.

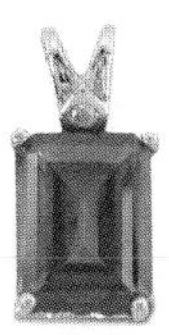

The octagon cut of this teal green Topaz dramatically promotes the clarity of the gem

TOPAZ

Topaz is mentioned in the Bible under Exodus and Ezekiel:

Exodus 28:17

And thou shalt set in it settings of stones, even four rows of stones: the first row shall be a sardius, a topaz, and a carbuncle: this shall be the first row.

Ezekiel 28:13

Thou hast been in Eden the garden of God; every precious stone was thy covering, the sardius, topaz, and the diamond, the beryl, the onyx, and the jasper, the sapphire, the emerald, and the carbuncle, and gold: the workmanship of thy tabrets and of thy pipes was prepared in thee in the day that thou wast created.

A Topaz powder ground into wine was believed to relieve asthma. Leaving a Topaz crystal in wine for three days produced an elixir that was used on the eyes to improve vision.

Some once believed that Topaz could make you invisible during moments of danger.

Clear, terminated Topaz was referred to as an Iris stone because of its double refractive qualities and the way its facets would project the light's rainbow spectrum. If worn in a ring on the left hand, the gem was believed to restrain lustful desires.

If you are on a journey of spiritual change, Topaz is believed by crystal healers to make an excellent companion. It apparently teaches you to trust in the Universe, aiding you to fully recognise the magical laws of attraction, increasing your ability to manipulate them.

Topaz is believed to strengthen confidence, to help in making correct decisions and to give courage in following through on choices, thereby changing dreams into reality.

Meditations with Topaz are believed by some to help awaken sleeping gifts and illuminate co-creative energies.

Just the facts

Its unique crystal structure makes Topaz a hard and dense gemstone and, because of this, pure

Champagne Topaz majestically flanked by Yellow Sapphires

The contrasting tones of blue in these gems are drawn out by using a chic white gold setting

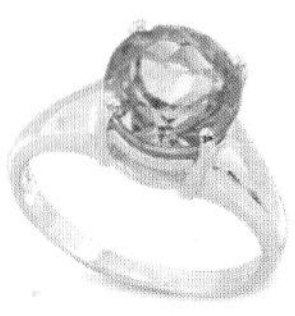

Strikingly faceted London Blue Topaz

Nigerian Topaz perfectly balanced in white and blue

clear Topaz has often been mistaken for Diamond. The huge Braganza gemstone (it weighs 1,680 carats) mounted into the Portuguese crown jewels was originally thought to be a Diamond; in fact it is a beautiful clear Topaz.

Topaz is found around the globe in Australia, Brazil, Russia, Sri Lanka, Japan, Nigeria, Mozambique, Pakistan, Norway and China.

Blue Topaz

As well as the renowned Sky Blue Topaz, the more intense colouring of Swiss Blue and London Blue Topaz makes them a favourite of the collectors.

It is believed to work with the throat chakra allowing you to voice the perfect words for bringing your desires and dreams into reality. It is also believed to unite body, mind and spirit.

Imperial Topaz

These gems often contain chromium and are sometimes heat-treated to bring out a rosy-red to pink hue in the gem.

Imperial Topaz is believed by some to be a gemstone of fire, burning with the energies of the Sun. It is also believed to replenish lost energy, stimulating the first three chakras, opening the crown.

White Topaz

Most Topaz is found in its purest form, clear. This is sometimes referred to as Silver or White Topaz. It is believed to be the gem of confidence, helping stimulate natural gifts.

Rose or Pink Topaz

Occasionally occurring naturally, Pink Topaz is believed to open the base chakra and balance the exhausting energies of passion and power. It is further believed by crystal healers that people who are quick to get angry will benefit from carrying a Pink Topaz as it can help control temper and channel anger into productive resolutions instead of fights.

Mystic Topaz

No other gemstone can compare to the kaleidoscope of colours witnessed in Mystic Topaz.

TOPAZ

The natural colour of Imperial Topaz is greatly complemented by this 18k yellow gold setting

By teaming it with Blue Sapphires our designers have enhanced the colourful hues of this Brazilian Mystic Topaz

TOPAZ:	November's birthstone
Locations:	Brazil, Mozambique, Nigeria, Australia, Russia, Sri Lanka, Japan, Pakistan, Norway, China
Colours Found:	Pink, blue, yellow, orange-pink, green, blue-green, white, bi-colour
Typical Cuts:	All cuts
Family:	Topaz
Hardness:	8.00
Refractive Index:	1.60 - 1.63
Relative Density:	3.50 - 3.60

TOURMALINE

The name Tourmaline comes from the Sinhalese word "Turmali" meaning "Mixed", due to its ability to appear in over 100 hues resulting in a historical tendency for it to be confused and then mixed with other gem varieties.

Although it may not be the world's most famous gemstone, Tourmaline rivals all but the most unique gems as it is found in an incredible array of gorgeous colours. This has resulted in the nickname "The Chameleon Gem", doubly appropriate when you consider that one major source of Tourmaline is Madagascar, home to more than half of the world's Chameleon species!

Coming in a palette of over 100 different colours, Tourmaline, with the exception of Quartz-based gems, is the most diverse gem type in the world. Although Tourmaline is not as well known as its counterparts Ruby, Sapphire and Emerald, in reality, the beauty of Tourmaline in all its shades and nuances is every bit as precious.

The amazing emerald green colour found in Brazilian Chrome Tourmaline

Legends and lore

Sri Lanka (formerly Ceylon) was also partly responsible for Tourmaline's first appearance in Europe, when Tourmaline gems were sold to Dutch traders who imported them to the West in the 1600s.

A stylish setting makes this Chrome Tourmaline ring a highly desired piece

The Dutch, aside from admiring Tourmaline for its beauty, first discovered that the gem possessed a unique property. Tourmaline, when heated or rubbed, creates an electrical charge, becoming a magnet that attracts lightweight objects.

Precisely hand cut the Tourmaline gems in these earrings shine with natural lustre

Today, Tourmaline's special property, known as piezoelectricity, has been incorporated into modern technologies such as computers, musical keyboards, cellular phones and other hi-tech devices.

Just the facts

An unusual 18k white gold prong setting holds this massive 29.4ct Cat's Eye Tourmaline

Tourmalines occur in large crystal sizes. Because of their size, crystals are usually cut into long rectangular shapes following the axis of the crystal.

Tourmaline crystals occur in granite pegmatite veins occurring in the great gem mining districts of Minas Gerias in Brazil, and the East African countries of Kenya, Tanzania, Mozambique, Malawi and Madagascar.

In the summer of 1998 a new Tourmaline deposit was unearthed near the city of Ibadan in Nigeria, West Africa, proving to be one of the most significant Tourmaline discoveries in modern times.

Tourmaline is a group of mineral species. However, it's the mineral Elbaite that is responsible for almost all of Tourmaline's most famous gem varieties. Elbaite frequently refers to Green Tourmaline, while the other colour forms of Elbaite have their own specific colour-related names.

Very occasionally, Tourmaline sometimes displays the cat's eye effect. Chatoyancy, or the cat's eye effect, is a reflection effect that appears as a single bright band of light across the surface of a gemstone.

Bi Colour & Tri Colour Tourmaline

Occurring in infinitesimal colour variations, they are often seen in long circular crystals.

Beautiful variations, zones and colour bands in Tourmaline are often purposefully accented by cutting styles to showcase the attractive bands and zones of colour streaking across the gem.

Green Tourmaline

Typically inclusion-free, Green Tourmaline offers gem consumers everything they want in an Emerald, but with more clarity.

Green Tourmaline have become very popular with collectors over recent years as they realise that this beautiful gem has yet to realise its true potential. Chrome Tourmaline is a more expensive variety of Green Tourmaline that bears Chromium, the Midas element responsible for producing particularly striking colours in a variety of gemstones.

This dramatic design is made up of 7 oval cut Multi-Coloured Tourmaline

A distinctive 'twisted' design containing 12 colour matched Tourmaline gems

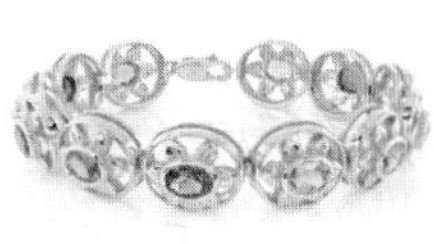

The mixture of colours and unusual settings gives this bracelet a young and modern edge

TOURMALINE

21 round cut Pink Tourmaline are used to create this arresting design

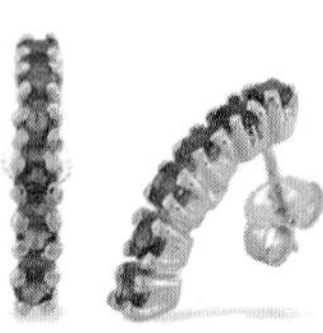

12 Perfectly colour matched Pink Tourmaline

TOURMALINE:	October's birthstone
Locations:	Nigeria, Brazil, Madagascar, Sri Lanka, Kenya, Tanzania, Malawi, Mozambique
Colours Found:	Fancy
Typical Cuts:	All cuts
Family:	Tourmaline
Hardness:	7.00 - 7.50
Refractive Index:	1.62 - 1.64
Relative Density:	3.06

Indicolite Tourmaline (Neon Blue)

This blue variety of Tourmaline offers gem and jewellery connoisseurs large gems at incredible value. Ranging from bright blue hues to bluish green colours, Indicolite Tourmaline is rarer than some of its coloured brothers and sisters, and high quality specimens are regarded as highly collectable.

Paraiba Tourmaline

So rare as to be virtually unattainable, Paraiba Tourmaline is a neon green copper bearing variety of Tourmaline from Paraiba in Brazil.

Rubellite Tourmaline (Red)

Rubellite's sensuous mélange is the personification of seduction, no other colours display incomparable feminine flair. Whispering in passionate pinks and suggestive purples, Rubellite affords the perfect romance in an opulence of red. Once aware of the extravagance and beauty of this gemstone, a woman can not be parted from her Rubellite, a gem of seduction (see page 91).

Watermelon Tourmaline

Colour variations in a crystal's cross-section sometimes have distinct concentric triangular or hexagonal patterns, where a pink core is surrounded by a green rind.

The effect is somewhat reminiscent of the green skins and pinkish flesh of watermelons. They are often cut into thin slices to showcase this colour effect to their best advantage.

What our Craftsmen say:

Miss Amphorn Santamyae - Polishing

"With a hardness of 7-7.5, this multitudinous gem is ideal for all types of jewellery setting. Tourmaline earrings, Tourmaline necklaces, Tourmaline rings and other types of Tourmaline jewellery are all well-suited to every day wear."

TURQUOISE

The name Turquoise is derived from the French "Pierre Turquois" meaning "Turkish Stone". This is because Western Europeans mistakenly thought the gem came from Turkey. In actual fact it came from the Sinai Peninsula or Alimersai Mountain in Persia (now Iran), which has been mining Turquoise since 5000 BC. In Persian, Turquoise is known as "Ferozah", meaning victorious and it is the national gemstone of Iran to this day.

Legends and lore

In Ancient times the Egyptians, Persians, Mongols and Tibetans all valued Turquoise highly. The first millennium AD saw a big increase in the popularity of Turquoise with both the Chinese and Native Americans becoming captivated by the blue stone.

This piece shows how our designers are inspired by many cultures

Turquoise was used for thousands of years as jewellery by the ancient Egyptians, who buried fine pieces with mummies. They began mining Turquoise in the Sinai Peninsula around 5500 BC.

When the tomb of Queen Zer was unearthed in 1900, a Turquoise and gold bracelet was found on her wrist, making this one of the oldest pieces of jewellery on Earth!

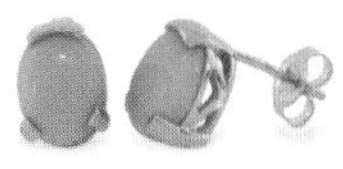

Tibetan Turquoise set into shamelessly elegant 9k gold earrings

In Asia, it was considered protection against the evil eye. Tibetans carved Turquoise into ritual objects as well as wearing it in traditional jewellery. Ancient manuscripts from Persia, India, Afghanistan and Arabia report that the health of a person wearing Turquoise can be assessed by variations in the colour of the gem. Turquoise was also thought to promote prosperity.

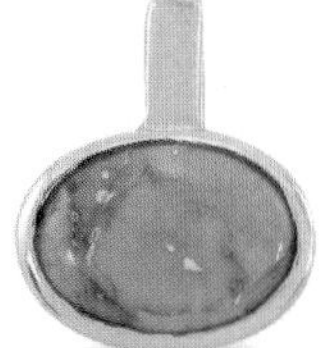

The veins of colour in this attractive pendant gives this gem the nickname 'spider web Turquoise'

It is also believed that Turquoise helps one to start new projects and protects the wearer from falling, especially from horses! In Europe even today, Turquoise rings are given as forget-me-not gifts.

Legend has it that some Native Americans believed that, if Turquoise was affixed to a bow, the arrows shot from it would always hit their mark.

The cabochon cut of Turquoise shows this gems natural lustre

TURQUOISE

The White Topaz and bar setting provides this Turquoise piece a noble looking finish

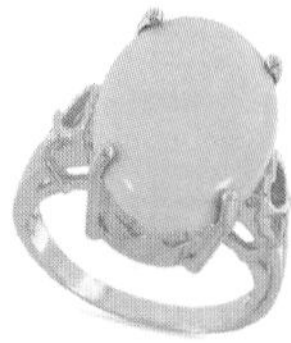

6ct of Turquoise set onto delicately detailed shoulders

A blend of white gold and boldly coloured Turquoise demonstrates that our designers just keep getting it right

TURQUOISE:	December's birthstone
Locations:	U.S.A, India, Afghanistan, China, Iran, Russia, France, Germany, Chile, Egypt, England, Australia
Colours Found:	Clear sky blue, green
Typical Cuts:	Cabochons, beads, ornamentals
Family:	Turquoise
Hardness:	5.00 - 6.00
Refractive Index:	1.61 - 1.65
Relative Density:	2.60 - 2.80

The blue of Turquoise was thought to have powerful metaphysical properties by many ancient cultures. Montezuma's treasure, now displayed in the British Museum, includes a fantastic carved serpent covered by a mosaic of Turquoise. In ancient Mexico, Turquoise was reserved for the gods, it could not be worn by mere mortals.

Just the facts

Turquoise, a hydrated phosphate of copper and aluminium, is prized as a gemstone whose intense blue colour is often mottled with veins of brown limonite or black manganese oxide (commonly known as Spider Web Turquoise).

Turquoise jewellery in the U.S. has long been produced by Native Americans (Zuni and Navajo peoples). Today, Turquoise is prominently associated with Native American culture, particularly Zuni bracelets, Navajo concha belts, squash blossom necklaces and thunderbird motifs.

The Native American Jewellery or "Indian style" jewellery with Turquoise mounted in or with silver is actually relatively new. Some believe this style of jewellery was unknown prior to about 1880, when a white trader persuaded a Navajo craftsman to make Turquoise and silver jewellery using coin silver. Prior to this time, the Native Americans had made solid Turquoise beads, carvings and inlaid mosaics.

Turquoise is almost always opaque but rare, translucent gems are known to exist.

Turquoise is currently mined in Arizona and New Mexico, U.S.A, Australia, Afghanistan and Iran, which arguably produces the world's finest quality Turquoise. Other U.S. Turquoise occurs in the Mojave Desert of California, the Cerrillos Hills near Sante Fe in New Mexico and the sates of Arizona, Nevada, Utah and Colorado. Many of these deposits were mined centuries ago by Native Americans.

Sky blue Turquoise occurs in Iran and a green variety occurs in Tibet. Additional mines are in Cornwall in England, Siberia in Russia, France, Germany, Chile, Egypt and China.

ZIRCON

Zircon's name is either derived from the Arabic word "Zarkun" meaning "Red", or a combination of the ancient Persian words "Zar" (gold) and "Gun" (colour). Despite this name, Zircon actually occurs in a myriad of colours.

Zircon's brilliant lustre, fire and bright hues make it an enjoyable addition to any jewellery collection.

Legends and lore

Carved Zircon has been found in some of the most ancient archaeological sites.

Zircon has appeared in literature under a variety of names including Jargon (Yellow Zircon), Jacinth (Red Zircon), Matara Diamond (White Zircon), Starlite (Blue Zircon), Hyacinth (Blue Zircon) and Ligure.

This beautiful cross pendant contains 6 Colombian Blue Zircon gems

Zircon is first mentioned in the ancient Indian tale of the Kalpa Tree. Described by Hindu poets as the ultimate gift to the gods, it was a bright, glowing tree with bejewelled leaves of Zircon.

The gemstone of fiery starlight, Jewish legends say that Zircon was the name of the guardian angel sent to watch over Adam and Eve in the Garden of Eden.

A traditional four prong setting holds these simple oval cut Blue Zircon gems

The Roman historian, Pliny the Elder, compared Blue Zircon's colour to Hyacinth flowers. In the Bible, Zircon is one of the twelve gemstones set in the foundations of the city walls of Jerusalem. Andreas, Bishop of Caesurae, associated Zircon with the Apostle Simon.

An amazing blend of colour, Cambodian Blue Zircon and dazzling African Diamonds

Traditionally, Zircon is a gem of purity and innocence. Zircon is believed to promote inner peace while providing the wearer with wisdom, honour and riches. Legend also has it that a Zircon's loss of lustre is a warning of imminent danger.

Zircon's popularity grew dramatically in the 16th Century when Italian artisans featured the gem in jewellery designs. In the 1880's Blue Zircon was widely used in Victorian jewellery.

Matt McNamara in Cambodia

Matt McNamara, one of Gems TV's presenters, visited several Cambodian Zircon mines in

ZIRCON

The dark blue of the Sapphires flawlessly balances the icy blue colour of the Zircon

Another example of precision faceting to enhance the brilliance of our gems

ZIRCON:	December's birthstone
Locations:	Cambodia, Thailand, Nigeria, Thailand, Vietnam, Sri Lanka
Colours Found:	Rainbow
Typical Cuts:	All cuts
Family:	Zircon
Hardness:	7.50
Refractive Index:	1.93 - 1.98
Relative Density:	4.60 - 4.70

2004, "I was amazed at how primitive some mines still are today. Because of the low prices that we sell gem set jewellery for at Gems TV, it's easy to forget how much work goes into unearthing these wonderful gems".

Just the facts

Although Zircon's existence predates Cubic Zirconia by centuries, Zircon is often unfairly confused with Cubic Zirconia. Cubic Zirconia is a cheap, synthetic Diamond substitute that resembles colourless Zircon and has a similar sounding name. While Zircon may also be used as a Diamond substitute, it is valuable in its own right.

The fire in Zircon, called dispersion, is caused by light entering the gemstone and separating into a prism of rainbow colours. Possessing dispersion approaching that of Diamond, the brilliance of Zircon is second to none. The Zircon Cut, a variation of the Brilliant Cut that adds eight extra facets to the pavilion, was designed to take advantage of these properties.

A very unique characteristic of Zircon is birefringence (doubly refractive), meaning that light splits into two rays as it passes through the gem. As a result, the back facets appear as double images.

Zircon is mined in Thailand, Vietnam, Cambodia, Sri Lanka and Nigeria. In fact, deposits of Zircon have even been found on the moon!

Cambodia is arguably the world's premiere source for gorgeous Zircon. Sixty-three miles North of Angkor Wat, close to the Cambodian-Thai border, lie the mines of Preah Vihear, the source of some of the world's finest Blue Zircon. Remote, primitive and stunningly beautiful, Ratanakiri is another major centre for Cambodian Zircon. Ratanakiri literally means "Gemstone Mountain". South of the city, a mining camp has been carved from the forest, where workers toil to extract Blue Zircon from narrow mine shafts that tap into an alluvial layer about 15 feet below the surface.

In addition to this guide, we are constantly updating our website with details on new deposits and new gem discoveries. While we don't have enough space to detail every gemstone, simply click on our "Gemstone Buyer's Guide" at www.GemsTV.com for full details on the following gems:

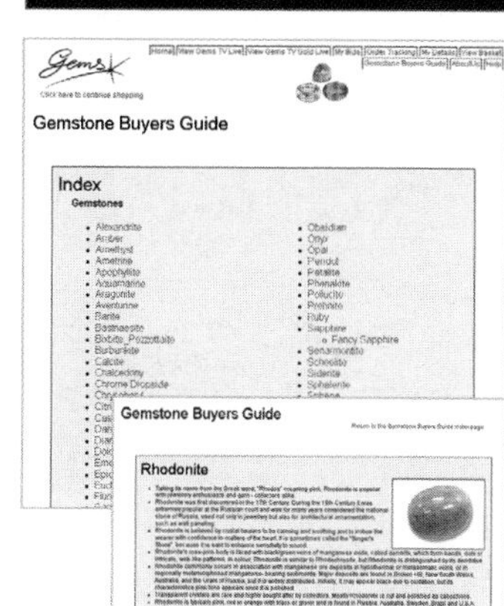

- Anapaite
- Anglesite
- Apophyllite
- Aragonite
- Axinite
- Azurite
- Barite
- Bastnaesite
- Bloodstone
- Boracite
- Burbankite
- Bustamite
- Calcite
- Cancrinite
- Carletonite
- Celestite
- Cerussite
- Charoite
- Chrysocolla
- Cinnabar
- Cobalt Calcite
- Creedite
- Datolite
- Dolomite
- Dumortierite
- Ekanite
- Enstatite
- Epidote
- Euclase
- Eudialyte
- Genthelvite
- Gibeon Meteorite
- Goshenite
- Hauyne
- Hematite
- Hemimorphite
- Hexagonite
- Indicolite
- Larimar
- Leifite
- Magnesite
- Mammoth Ivory
- Marcasite
- Mellite
- Milarite
- Monazite
- Montebrasite
- Mookite
- Natrolite
- Nuummit
- Oligoclase
- Parisite
- Pectolite
- Petalite
- Phenakite
- Pollucite
- Prasiolite
- Prehnite
- Pyrite
- Pyroxmangite
- Remondite
- Rhodochrosite
- Rhodonite
- Rutile
- Sard
- Sardonyx
- Scheelite
- Senarmontite
- Serandite
- Shortite
- Siderite
- Sinhalite
- Smithsonite
- Spectrolite
- Sphalerite
- Spodumene
- Staurolite
- Sugilite
- Thaumasite
- Tremolite
- Tugtupite
- Unakite
- Villaumite
- Willemite
- Wulfenite

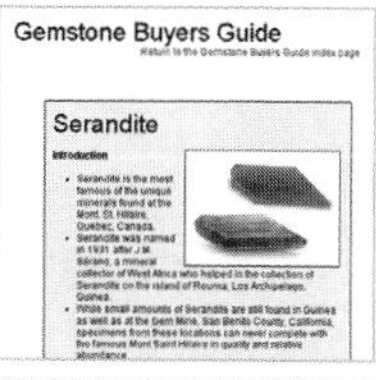

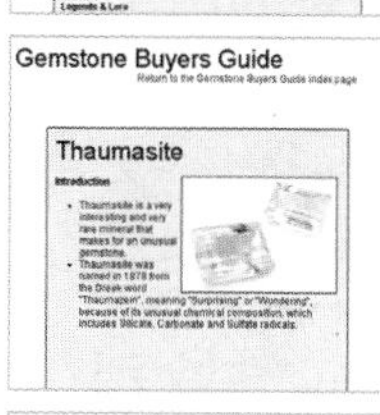

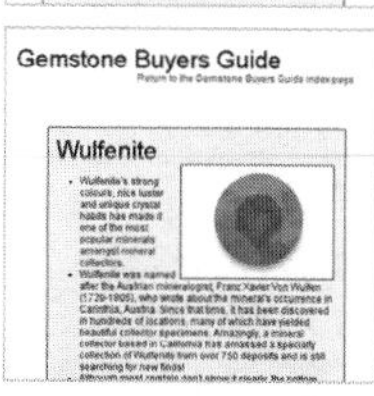

JEWELLERY VALUATIONS

"Last week I made my first purchase with you. I paid £89 for an Alexandrite and Opal ring. I was so delighted, but took your advice and had the ring valued. The valuation came back at £475! Really pleased with your services, keep up the good work."

Nicola, Aughton
15th June 2005

"I am absolutely delighted to tell you about the valuations I have just received. I purchased a Pink Sapphire ring for £64, now valued at £550. Just this week I purchased a Pink Sapphire & Blue Topaz pendant for £99. It has been valued at £790. I can't wait to complete my set with a pair of Pink Sapphire earrings. Your jewellery is superb, I've even got my husband hooked."

Ann, Merseyside
7th June 2005

"In March I bought my mum for her birthday a Green and Blue Sapphire ring... I paid £76 and they valued it at £575. I think what you are doing is fantastic. I had never been that much into jewellery before, and then I started watching a few weeks after your launch and I am hooked big time and I love it."

Sue, Kent
9th June 2005

Steve Bennett of Gems TV shares his views on getting jewellery valued....

The Oxford Dictionary says that a valuation is an "estimation of a thing's worth".

As you will probably want to insure the jewellery you purchase from us for the cost of replacement and not the low price that you paid for it, it often means that you have to seek an independent valuation from a local jeweller.

Before seeking independent valuations please take the following points into consideration:

Basis for valuation

What is the basis of the valuation? It could be said that a valuation is really what someone is prepared to pay for something. For example, what is the value of the Mona Lisa? Is the value the same as the cost of the canvas and the paint or is it determined by the amount which someone will pay for it? We believe that valuations for jewellery should reflect the average cost you would have to pay to replace the item if lost or stolen.

It is my opinion that the ONLY way to achieve a true valuation is to ask a jeweller to make an exact replica of the piece of jewellery. Tell them "I want it as a gift for a friend who likes mine". Tell them it must be identical in carat weight, similar in colour, similar in clarity, cut etc, also tell them that it must have the same gold weight.

Tell them "please put the price in writing and write down that you guarantee to honour the price for 30 days, in order for me to check that my friend is happy". What you now have in your hand is an independent valuation.

Independent

On these pages you will read just a handful of the thousands of comments received by letter and email from delighted customers who have informed us that they have received valuations way beyond our start price (let alone the price they paid for it). However, we have also had others that have commented that their local jeweller had provided a valuation below that of their expectations. This comes as no surprise to us at Gems TV, as the question is "Is a local jeweller the right person to give a true independent opinion on a product that has been supplied by possibly their biggest enemy?"

As soon as they see our hallmark on an item, you can rest assured that they will not be feeling very independent.

Knowledge

Although most independent jewellers will have a good understanding of valuing gold, silver and diamonds, many will not have even seen some of the precious stones that you will purchase from Gems TV.

With a lack of understanding of how to value such items as Tanzanite and Alexandrite, you may struggle to get a valuation that has any real accuracy.

Comprehensive

To achieve a comprehensive valuation, in most cases, a jeweller would need to dismantle the jewellery to calculate an accurate carat weight of each gem and to check all of the gem's cuts which due to their being set in the jewellery are not visible to the naked eye. The Oxford dictionary describes the word assessment as "estimate the size, value or quality of", how would it be possible to asses the size or cut of a gem without removing it? To avoid the jeweller having to do this, feel free to show them your "Authenticity Card" that we ship with all of our designs.

Fear of making a mistake

Like every profession, jewellers are fearful of making a professional mistake. If you tell a jeweller how little you paid for an item, they will find it very difficult to provide you with an unbiased judgement.

"A few weeks ago I bought a Sapphire and Diamond ring for just £37. I had took it to a jewellers who valued it at £750! Will keep watching the show, I think all the birthday and Christmas presents for the rest of this year will probably be bought from Gems TV!"

Sarah, Harwick
15th June 2005

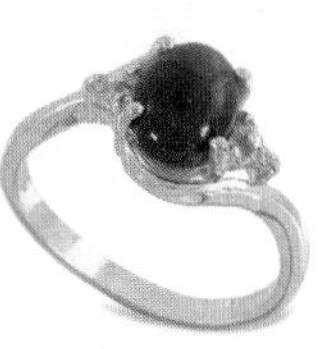

"I recently bought a lovely Aquamarine ring...and took it to my local jewellers to be resized...The lady owner of the shop estimated £65 to replace one stone. As I had only paid £48 for the ring, I was interested then to see what her valuation of the whole ring would be. She quoted £1000 to make me a copy in case of theft or loss!"

Heather, Nottingham
6th June 2005

"I purchased off you a pair of 9ct gold Ruby earrings which cost £33. I had them valued and they were valued at £195. I also purchased a 9ct gold Ruby and Diamond bracelet which cost £89 and that was valued at £275. I couldn't believe the savings I have made by shopping with you thank you all so much I will definitely be shopping with Gems TV again"

Paul, Dorset
21st July 2005

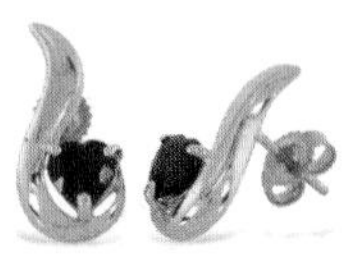

JEWELLERY VALUATIONS

"I would just like to let you know that I recently had an insurance valuation done on an 18K Diamond white gold ring. I paid £488 for it. I was so pleased when the valuation came back and was for £1200. I bought the ring to wear on my little finger and I am so happy with the quality, I am even MORE happy with it now I have had it valued !!! Thanks for the excellent service & keep up the great work."

Steve, Notts
1st August 2005

"I bought a 18 carat gold Sapphire carving and Diamond gold pendant last week and paid £50, I've just had it valued at an amazing price of £800. I'm extremely over the moon and ordered another. I've lost count on how many brilliant rings I've bought from you and watch both your channels every day."

Paula, Kent
24th July 2005

"I purchased a fantastic Fancy Sapphire ring for £299 and a stunning Pink Topaz ring at £79. The first ring has come back valued at £1700 and the second ring £225. Value is important but for me it's a bonus as I love your jewellery and will continue to add to my collection... Thanks Gems TV."

Angela, Northumberland
28th July 2005

As Gems TV is a manufacturer of handcrafted jewellery that sells direct to the consumer, cutting out numerous middlemen, our customers are assured that they are buying jewellery at a fraction of what they would pay for similar high quality products via normal means. What's more, as one of the largest suppliers of gems in the world, in most cases, we are able to buy our gems direct from the mines. As the average gemstone is traded some 9 to 14 times before it reaches the consumer, it is possible for many gems to suffer over a 1,000% increase in price on its convoluted route from the mine to the consumer

A changing world

Because Gems TV is unique and because Gems TV has introduced a new cost-effective way of selling jewellery, many jewellers are unable to comprehend how we do it (especially those who are in direct competition with us). Whilst some independent jewellers thank us for increasing the awareness of coloured gemstones and therefore growing consumer demand, other short-sighted jewellers actively try to discredit our services and our products. Please bear this in mind when seeking valuations.

On page 191 we have details of valuers that have been recommended by our customers.

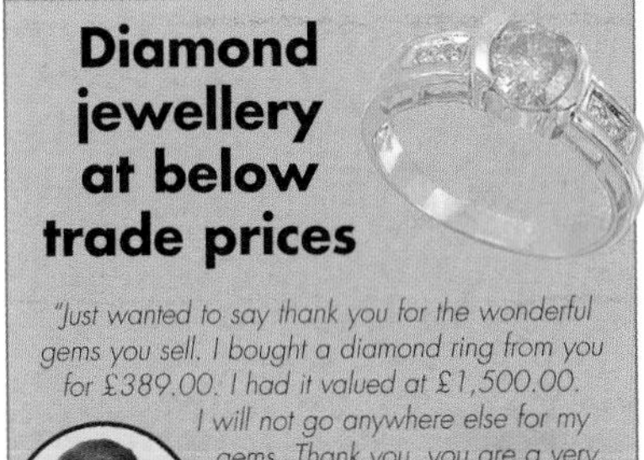

ZODIAC GEMS

Originating in ancient India, below is a correlation of gems with the astrological signs.

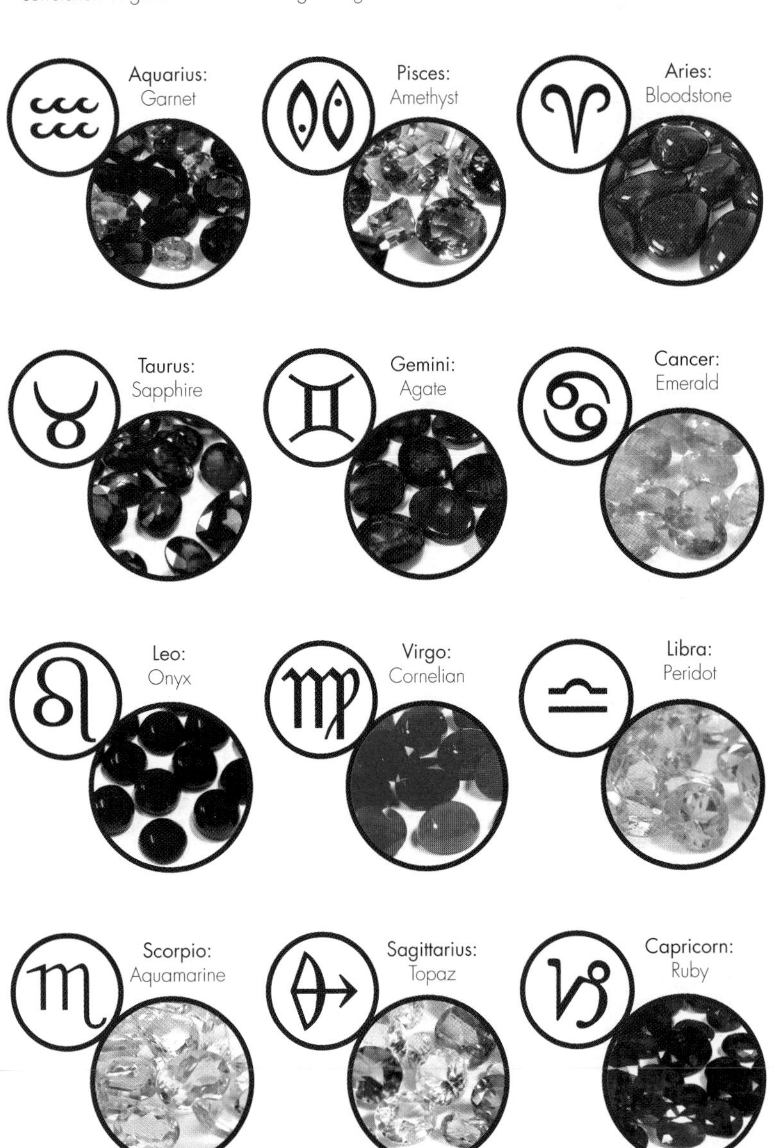

BIRTHSTONE GEMS

January's birthstone:
Sacred Garnet, the zodiac gem of Aquarius, is cited in the Holy Bible as the gemstone that delivered Noah and his ark to salvation. Garnets are believed to act as healing gems that both protect and strengthen the wearers' spiritual and emotional powers. Available in a myriad of rich tones from full-bodied reds and oranges to verdant greens, Garnet's warmth brings a welcome glow to the cold winter months.

February's birthstone:
Amethyst, the zodiac gem of Pisces, is said to be the preferred gemstone of St. Valentine. Favoured by queens and coveted by kings the intense lavender-purple hues of Amethyst are believed to possess magical properties that promote wisdom, courage, quickening of the wit and sharpening of the mind. Enduringly popular, Amethyst is a gemstone of legend whose lore is only surpassed by its beauty.

March's birthstone:
Aquamarine, gemstone of the sea god Poseidon and the zodiac gem of Scorpio, has mesmerised all who gaze into its fathomless tones. The seafarers of old believed that when faced with tempestuous seas, casting offerings of Aquamarine into the ocean would placate Poseidon's anger. A gem of cleansing and purification, Aquamarine's scintillating colour and clarity are said to bring peace and happiness and aid the renewal of relationships.

April's birthstone:
"Diamonds are Forever", sang Shirley Bassey, while Marilyn insisted they were "A Girl's Best Friend". Celebrated in song, Diamond has long reigned as the ultimate statement of ardour and affection. Believed to be the tears of the Gods, splinters from falling stars or the prodigy of lightning struck rocks, the myths and legends associated with Diamonds continue to transcend both cultures and continents.

May's birthstone:
The green fire of Emerald, zodiac gem of Cancer, has been associated with rejuvenation for more than 3,000 years. Venerated by Aztec high priests and coveted by the crown heads of Europe, Emerald occupies a hallowed place in gemstone history. Emeralds are believed to have powerful metaphysical properties affecting both the conscious and unconscious mind, strengthening memory and increasing psychic awareness.

June's birthstones:
Pearl, Moonstone and Alexandrite, signalling the start of summer, present a trilogy of gems that reflect the wonders of the sea, sky and earth. Cleopatra bewitched Marc Anthony with a love potion of ground salt water Pearls, while Moonstone's mystical iridescence captivated ancient civilisations who believed its play of light was due to spirits living within this celestial gem. Terrestrial Alexandrite continues to mesmerise all who lay eyes upon its extraordinary colour-change.

July's birthstone:
A symbol of kingship, passion and romance, Ruby's velvety crimson hues saw them named "Rajnapura" or "King of Gems" by the ancient Hindus. Mined for over 2,500 years, the ancient Burmese believed that Rubies generated mystical forces and were thus a powerful protector from harm. Gemstone to Capricorns, Rubies were also believed to contain prophetic powers, enabling wearers to predict the future based on changes in their colour intensity.

August's birthstone:
Peridot, the gemstone of Librans, were believed by the ancient Hawaiians to be the goddess Pele's tears, while biblical references to the gem include the high priest's breastplate. Ottoman Sultans gathered the world's largest collection of Peridot during their 600 year reign. Peridot was once believed to possess the power to protect the wearer from spells, promote tranquil sleep, provide foresight and give divine inspiration.

BIRTHSTONE GEMS

September's birthstone:

The zodiac gem to Taurus, Sapphire, "Gem of the Heavens", comes in every colour of the rainbow, from the traditional blues to a myriad of fancy colours. Sapphires are emotionally linked to calmness and loyalty, explaining their popularity in engagement rings. The guardians of innocence, Sapphires symbolise truth, sincerity and faithfulness, and are thought to bring peace, joy and wisdom to their owners.

October's birthstones:

Tourmaline and Opal bless those born in October with a cornucopia of colour. Described as the "Chameleon Gemstone", Tourmaline comes in an unparalleled kaleidoscope of colours. Many refer to Tourmaline as the "Muses' Gemstone", as they believe its imaginative colours contain inspirational powers. Opal's unique play of colour has intrigued civilisations since the dawn of time, with the ancient Arabs believing that Opals had fallen from heaven in flashes of lightning.

November's birthstones:

November babies can celebrate with a colourful pairing of two of the world's perennial favourites, Citrine and Topaz. Taking its name from the French word for lemon, the ancient Greeks and Romans believed Citrine's vibrant golden tones were symbolic of happiness. While Topaz, the zodiac gem of Sagittarius, was called the "Gem of the Sun" by the ancient Egyptians who believed it coloured by the golden glow of their sun god Ra.

December's birthstones:

From ancient traditions to contemporary fashion, cool blues and vivid purples are combined in the unmistakable beauty of Turquoise, Zircon and Tanzanite. While 7,000 year old Turquoise jewellery had been found in the tomb of an Egyptian Queen, it was a mere 1,000 years ago that the fire of Zircon mesmerised the ancient Khmer. A thousand times rarer than Diamonds and with a only decade of mining remaining, Tanzanite is the fashion gem of the millennium.

ANNIVERSARY GEMS

Although these gems are associated with wedding anniversaries, many people give them as gifts to celebrate all kinds of anniversaries.

1st
Gold
Jewellery

2nd
Garnet

3rd
Pearls

4th
Blue
Topaz

5th
Sapphire

6th
Amethyst

7th
Onyx

8th
Tourmaline

9th
Lapis Lazuli

10th
Diamond
Jewellery

11th
Turquoise

12th
Jade

14th
Opal

15th
Ruby

16th
Peridot

17th
Amethyst

18th
Cat's Eye
Beryl

19th
Garnet

20th
Emerald

21st
Iolite

22nd
Spinel

23rd
Imperial
Topaz

24th
Tanzanite

25th
Silver
Jubilee

30th
Pearl Jubilee

35th
Emerald

39th
Cat's Eye

40th
Ruby

45th
Sapphire

50th
Golden
Jubilee

52nd
Star Ruby

55th
Alexandrite

60th
Diamond
Jubilee

65th
Star
Sapphire

70th
Sapphire
Jubilee

75th
Diamond

WHAT IS A GEM?

Although Diamonds are nowhere near as rare as most people believe, they score very highly in beauty and durability. The Diamond pictured above is from the Cullinan Diamond Mine

For decades, the Gemological Institute of America (GIA) has taught their students that: "gems are specimens of minerals or organic materials used for personal adornment that possess the attributes of **beauty, rarity,** and **durability**."

The GIA teaches that all three of these attributes must be present – a gem lacking in one or more of these attributes risks losing its status as a gem.

Beauty

In loose gems, strength of colour is probably the most important factor. Strong colours are expected in the majority of gems, including Ruby, Emerald and Sapphire. However, Kunzite and Aquamarine aren't typically known for strength of colour, yet are greatly appreciated when they display rich and deep colour.

Amethyst

Tanzanite

This making of a gem's colour saturation such an important issue limits the potential of less-saturated gem material. For example, lightly-coloured Amethyst, while attractive as light Tanzanite, was traditionally considered among the least valuable of all gems.

In transparent gems, the degree of transparency and light return (brilliance) is considered crucial. However, through market experience, we learn to expect certain degrees of clarity from certain gems. For example, Aquamarine is generally expected to be clean and Emerald is expected to be hazy. Flawless, clean Emeralds are very rare. generally jewellery retailers tend to sell the more transparent Emeralds at a huge premium.

Alexandrite, Tanzanite and Padparadscha Sapphire are amongst some of the rarest gems in the world.

Rarity

"What is rare and beautiful is desired..."

Consider the success of Tourmaline from Paraíba, Brazil. Small, often highly included and now so rare that it is practically unavailable on the market, Paraíba Tourmaline broke all pricing rules and now commands higher per-carat prices than fine Sapphire and Diamond. Its remarkable and memorable electric-blue colour and publicity added to its cachet as a rare gem. However, rarity does not always add value. Sometimes the rarity of a gem type jeopardises commercial viability. Tsavorite Garnet is rarer than Emerald, is entirely free of treatments and is frequently more beautiful but, because there aren't enough around, cannot compete with Emerald in terms of the consumer's perception of its value.

Then consider Amethyst, a Quartz that is not considered rare. Often beautiful, clean, durable and colourful, its reasonable abundance brings its status as a gem into question. In Medieval Europe, Amethyst was rare and the colour purple was coveted but today Amethyst is typically only highly regarded by industry professionals when it appears in its top colours.

Given the enormous stockpiles and new sources springing up around the world, when compared to many coloured gemstones in this guide, Diamonds aren't very rare. Strict control of polished Diamonds on the market, combined with sophisticated consumer advertising, has elevated Diamonds to the extent that they are perceived as a rare and coveted product.

Today, Tsavorite Garnet is far rarer than Emerald yet still demands a slightly lower price.

Durability

"The love of precious gemstones is deeply implanted in the human heart," George Kunz wrote in his book The Curious Lore of Precious Stones, "The cause of this must be sought not only in their colouring and brilliancy but also their durability."

Kunz further wrote, "The sheen and colouration of precious stones are the same today as they were thousands of years ago and will be for thousands of years to come. In a world of change, this permanence has a charm of its own that was early appreciated."

A gemstone must be durable enough not to break or fade over years of wear. Its brilliance and beauty are expected to last for a very long time, even to the point where a gemstone will outlast its owners and be passed on to sons and daughters, which, in turn, will help maintain its status as a gem and awaken appreciation in the succeeding generations.

Given proper care all gemstone jewellery should be suitable to be passed down to many generations

GEM FORMATION

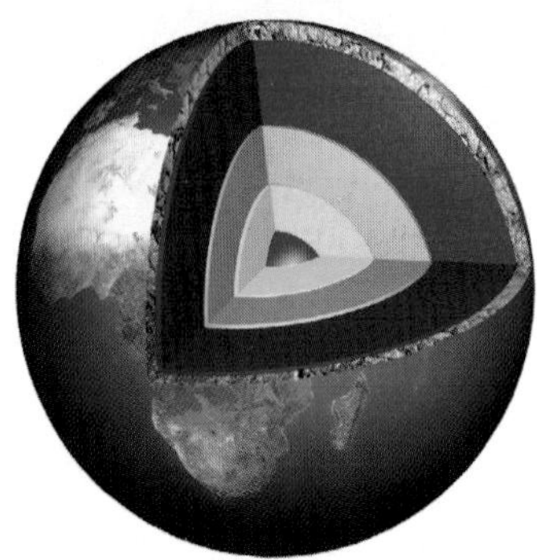

One of the most beautiful things about collecting natural gemstones is the thought that they are the creation of mother nature. The combination of gems and precious metals such as gold and silver sees the marriage of two natural sources, whose combined beauty is magnified as a couple.

At Gems TV, everything we sell is the real thing. In our past, we have often contemplated and even occasionally experimented with selling man made substitutes such as Cubic Zirconia and Moissanite, however, since June 2005, Gems TV decided that, to be successful in reaching its mission to become the largest coloured gemstone supplier in the world, selling anything but the real thing was not acceptable. As Steve Bennett, the Managing Director for Europe at Gems TV, puts it "In an attempt to sell jewellery to everyone, we added the gem equivalent of a toy car to our range. Over time, we realised that, by offering the Ferraris of the gem world at the prices of a family saloon, many thousands of people started to appreciate the merits of learning to drive, rather than pushing around toy cars".

So how are gems and precious metals created?

Most natural gemstones and precious metals are a product of the earth's crust. A few notable exceptions are Pearls (page 82) and Amber (page 13).

We all remember the 20 questions guessing game that we played as children, where the first question was animal, vegetable or mineral, well it is the latter of these three categories that 99% of all gemstones and metals fall into.

Minerals

Minerals are generally solid and are made from inorganic compounds (the most famous mineral that breaks these rules is water).

Mineral types vary by their atomic structure, crystal structure and chemical composition. Mineral gemstones (more than 99% of natural

Two famous organic gemstones that are not minerals are Pearl and Amber

gems) have a uniformed structure. Take Kyanite, for example. Its chemical composition is Al_2SiO_5, its harness is 5 to 7 and it has a perfect cleavage. Now, when miners and gemologists make a discovery, they initially look at the crystal shape, the crystal cleavage and the colour of the rough material in order to identify their discovery. Then, by testing its chemical composition, they are able to clearly define the exact gem type they have discovered.

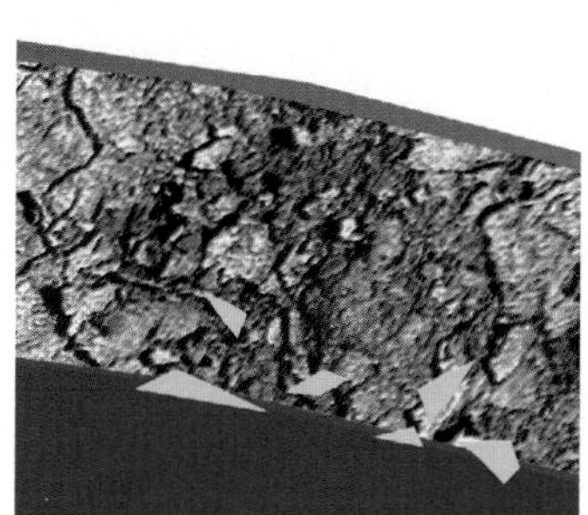

Where the crust and the mantle meet gems are often found

Crust

Upper Mantle

Gem Deposits

How are minerals first formed?

The earth's crust varies from 3 miles to 25 miles in thickness (5 to 40 kilometres). The crust tends to be thinner under seabeds and thicker under land. Under this thin layer of solid crust lies the fluid mantle. The best way to visualise the crust and the mantle is to imagine a very juicy orange. The mantle makes up approximately 83% of the earth's volume.

The mantle is fluid and composed of molten rock, (magma). When this breaks through the earths surface it is renamed lava. The mantle is hottest near the centre of the earth and the change in heat currents keep it in constant motion.

Where the mantle and crust meet is a very active and traumatic area. As you might recall from geography at school, all of the earth's crust is made up of plates that float and constantly move on the liquid mantle. As these plates collide with each other, some are pushed downwards and are re-melted by the intense temperature of the mantle and others are raised to form mountains.

As one plate is forced under the other, the upper plate creates mountains whilst the lower plate is forced into the mantle and is turned back to molten lava

Plates

Mantle

You can imagine what is constantly happening on the underside of the crust. With plates pushing down and molten racing by, many fractures and crevasses both appear and disappear. Some rocks break free from the crust and are carried away in the fluid magma. Many of them melt, changing the chemistry of the nearby magma. Some of the smaller particles even appear as inclusions in other gemstones.

As the molten rock cools, it crystallises. It is the

GEM FORMATION

When magma finds its way into cracks and crevices a multitude of different gems can be found

conditions of this cooling process that predominantly determine the fate of the rock. In most circumstances, its creation is of no interest to gemologists and wearers of fine jewellery but in a minute proportion of occurrences, Mother Nature will create the most beautiful gems.

It is important to point out that this cooling process can dramatically vary in time. Occasionally, molten will get trapped in a crevasse and will start to cool, its environment might then change and it might once again rise in temperature. When you see a gemstone with different colour bands, often this cooling and re-heating process is the cause.

As the molten cools, it will often crystallise in layers. Occasionally different layers will have different orientations (known as twinning). Some layers do not perfectly bond with other layers and this is the cause of a cleavage within a gemstone.

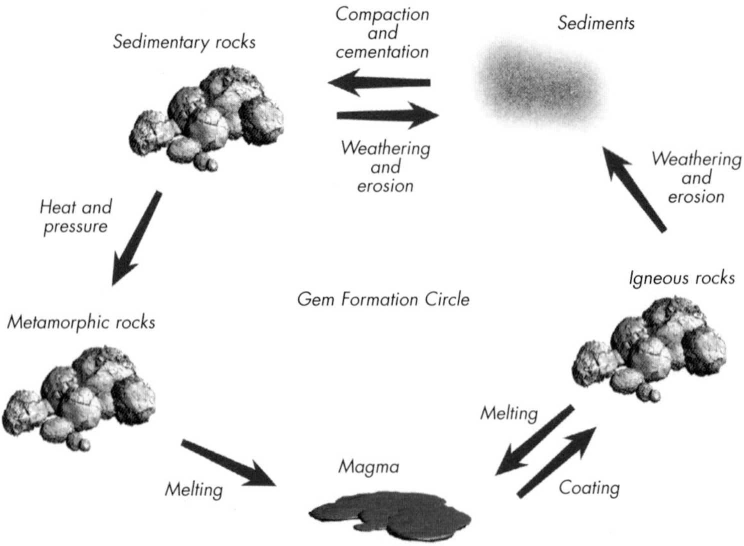

Because this cooling process is often a stop-start process, it is not uncommon for different layers to form different crystals. Take Madagascar for instance, the number of gems available from this one location is immense. This is not only due to the fact that over millions of years rocks travel on the earth's surface, but also because the environment in which the molten crystallised will have changing temperatures, changing pressures and, due to the constant movement of the molten, different chemistry.

A new crystal may start to grow on an existing crystal. Then the environment might change again and the original crystal starts growing again enclosing the other crystal which now appears as an inclusion.

Occasionally two different minerals will crystallise together. When this occurs one tends to become dominant and grows faster. When the gem is totally formed, the faster growing crystal will often engulf the other. This is how pyrite crystals are found inside Emeralds.

Because the earth's surface is constantly changing, not all rocks and gems that are discovered are formed from the initial crystallisation of molten.

All mineral gemstones are found in rocks and, of course, the rocks themselves are minerals. All rocks can be divided into three distinct groups:

Igneous

This type of rock is formed from molten rock called "magma", either below the surface of the earth (referred to as intrusive igneous rocks) or sometimes is externally exposed by such events as erupting volcanos which produce lava (the name given to magma once it reaches the surface of the earth).

Sedimentary

As Igneous rocks start to weather and erode, they become fragmented. Over millions of years, these fragments get compounded and reform as sedimentary rock. Often found in layers, not only do they make for stunning rock faces and tourist attractions, but also, on a smaller scale, create wonderful gems such as Opals.

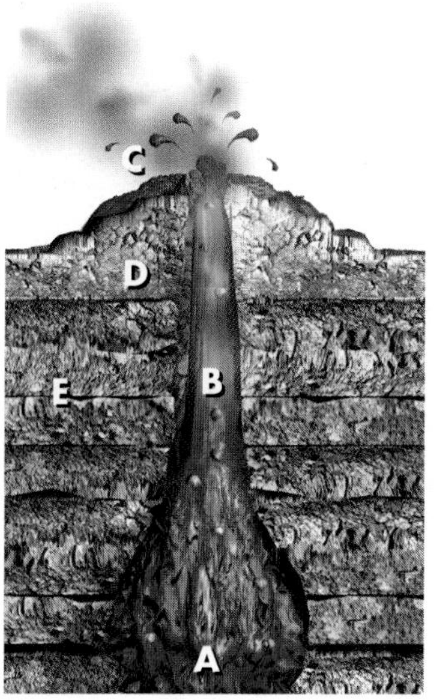

A *Diamonds are formed deep in the mantle*

B *Peridot occurs in upper volcanic activity*

C *Zircon, Rubies and Topaz can be formed in gas bubbles in exploding lava*

D *A multitude of gem varieties are discovered here*

E *Sedimentary deposits give us gems such as Opal*

GEM FORMATION

Metamorphic

These rocks started out life as either Igneous or Sedimentary and, under the right conditions, the temperature and pressure can rise to the point where existing minerals (rocks) are no longer stable. Under these conditions, minerals can change into different species without even melting. Rocks formed from this effect are known as metamorphic.

Why are gems rare?

But, with all rocks originating from very similar processes, why are so very few actually of gem quality? Why are they so rare?

The main reason is that the beautiful rare gems that we all love to collect and wear, are rarely formed purely in the magma itself! But, rather, are formed from fluids that escape from it or through other metamorphic processes.

Below are some of the main events that take place to form gems.

Opals, Amethysts and Agate are sometimes the bi-product of past rain falls

Gems created near the surface of the earth

Some gems are created by the effect of rain falling onto the earth's surface. Rain has the power to dissolve many minerals and transport various components within a liquid solution. In many areas in the world, after a rainy season, there is often a very barren dry period. When this occurs the water tables fall, leaving behind deposits of minerals such as Silica. Then, over millions of years, the resulting pressure applied by mother nature yields some stunning gemstones.

Gems such as Opals, Amethyst, Agate, Turquoise and Malachite are found in countries where this type of climate pattern is most pronounced!

Zircon, Rubies and Topaz are often created by gas crystallisation

Gas crystallisation

Although most gems grow on a solid base, others such as Garnets, Spinel and Topaz are often grown inside gas bubbles!

Imagine an erupting volcano as a bottle of

champagne being opened. As you remove the cork and the alcohol (lava) flies everywhere, gas bubbles are also being flung into the air. In some circumstances, these bubbles can contain high concentrations of certain elements. If the right combination of temperature and pressure exist for a long enough time, crystals form.

Hydrothermal

As water moves through the earth's crust, it begins to heat. The hotter it becomes the more minerals it is able to dissolve. When this chemical cocktail meets magma, new fluids are formed. As these new fluids move through fractures in the crust, they often begin to settle in veins. Hydrothermal gems include Emeralds and Beryls.

Gems from the Beryl family such as Emerald and Tourmaline are hydrothermally created

Magma crystallisation

The majority of minerals that are formed purely from the cooling of molten, are not of gem quality. However, occasionally, the chemical ingredients, temperature and pressure can work together to create some wonderful gems. If this cooling process is caused by the molten rushing towards the earth's surface due to the movement of plates or a volcano, it can result in the creation of such gems as Sapphires, Rubies and Moonstones. Because Diamonds crystallise at temperatures higher than all other minerals, it is now believed that they can actually form in moving magma, below the earth's crust. If this is found to be true, it means that the crystallisation of Diamonds is the most simple and the most common of all crystallisations on earth. It will also mean that Diamonds are the most common of all gemstones, but are just very difficult to reach!

Moonstones, Diamonds and Sapphires can be created by magma crystallisation

Steve Bennett, Gems TV MD says:

"Even though there are 1,000's of gem mines around the globe, I have calculated that most of the world's annual output of faceted coloured gemstones and Diamonds, if they we are all stored together, would not even fill one bus! "

In 2005, the global output of faceted Diamonds, Emeralds, Alexandrite, Tanzanite, Sapphires and Rubies, if all stored together, would not even fill the lower deck of a bus!

GEM CRYSTAL PROPERTIES

Mammoth tusks over 10,000 years old are examples of organic gemstones

Tourmaline has a macrocrystalline structure

Chrysoprase and Jade have polycrystalline structures

Gem crystal structures

All gemstones are broadly split into two categories that depend on their origin:

Type 1: Organic gemstones

These are gemstones that are natural materials which are formed by, or with the help of, organic life processes, such as animals or trees. Examples of organic gemstones are Pearls (from molluscs) and Amber (fossilised tree resin).

Type 2: Inorganic gemstones

This is by far the larger of the two categories. With virtually all other gem types belonging to this category; inorganic means no living organisms were involved in making the material. These gemstones come from an inorganic mineral origin. In simple terms, minerals are generally solid, inorganic, crystalline materials which are formed by geological processes.

Atoms and crystal structure

The earth consists of elements made up of countless atoms. Most of these atoms are in orderly, solid arrangements. Materials with such orderly atomic arrangements are said to be crystalline and each different atomic arrangement is called a crystal structure.

Most natural gem materials are crystalline – they possess crystal structure. Atoms bond together most efficiently as orderly crystal structures and they automatically try to pack into the most orderly structure possible. In simple terms a crystal structure is a regular, repeating, three-dimensional arrangement of bonded atoms.

Crystalline materials can be either:

1. Made from one single piece of crystal. Single-piece crystals are termed macrocrystalline. Most gemstones fall into this category, such as Ruby, Sapphire, Amethyst and Tourmaline.
2. Made up from different crystalline pieces that have come together or grown together.

Materials that consist of different crystals are termed polycrystalline. Examples are Jade, Agate and Chrysoprase.

Some of the resulting properties and phenomena from the possession of crystal structure include:

- Asterism (star effect)
- Chatoyancy (cat's eye effect)
- Colour Change
- Double Refraction
- Pleochroism

It is this possession of different crystal structures offered by many gemstones that gives them their unique properties. Without these unique properties, our ancestors would have never valued them as unusual, rare, desirable or beautiful and, in turn, today, without them, our gemstone choices would be very limited.

Cat's Eye Alexandrite uniquely demonstrates both colour change and chatoyancy

Asteric gem inclusions

Centre alignment

Off centre alignment

Asterism

Gemstones that show asterism include Corundum (Sapphires and Rubies), Almandine Garnet, Spinel, Quartz and Beryl.

Asterism or the star effect is caused by reflections from two or more sets of parallel fibrous or channel inclusions, orientated within a gemstone, which produces a 'star' effect on the surface of the gem, when cut into cabochon in a certain orientation.

It is the crystal structure of the gem that arranges the symmetrical placement of the impurities, causing 'asterism'.

Some gemstones will produce this effect when:

(a) the inclusions are long ('needle-shaped');

(b) the inclusions are in parallel arrangements in at least two different directions;

(c) the inclusions are sufficiently abundant;

(d) the gemstone is cut in such a way that the top is curved and the base is parallel to the direction in which the inclusions lie.

The reflection takes the form of two or more intersecting lines of light, depending on the

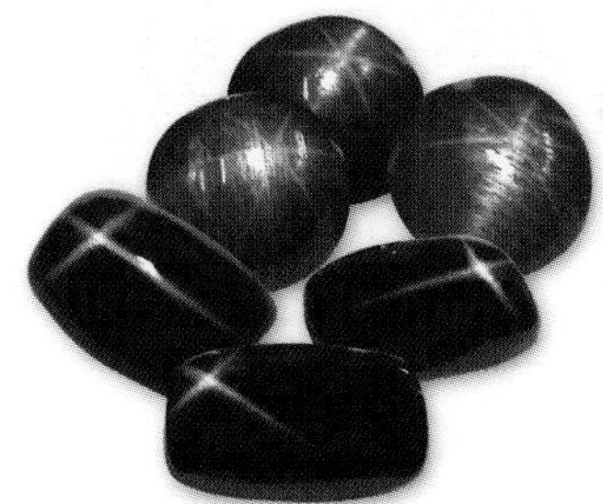

Star Diopside and Star Sunstone showing perfect asterism

Star Ruby and Star Sunstone demonstrating how gems with asterisms are always cabochon cut

Gems TV presenter Caroline Lyndsay (top) and Debby Cavill at the mine in Chanthaburi (only 7km from Gems TV's design centre). This is the only mine in the world where Black Star Sapphire is found.

Black Star Sapphire mine

The pride of Chanthaburi, a Black Star Sapphire

number of sets of parallel inclusions. The needles crystallise along the atomic planes at 120 degrees to each other, reflecting light back to the eye in a symmetrical and star like manner.

The quality and value of an asteriated gem is judged by:

1. The distinctiveness of its star
2. The length and degree of straightness of each ray
3. The strength & uniformity of the gem's colour
4. Where the star is (if the cabochon is not aligned properly when cut, the resulting effect is that the star will not be seen as being in the centre of the gemstone)
5. The gem's size and carat weight. However, in the cases this is done deliberately for artistic affect, particularly in non round cabochons

Asterism is most visible with direct light, such as a fibre-optic light, penlight or other single beam of light, including direct sunlight. With diffused illumination, the stars are not as distinct (often a problem under TV studio lights).

Chatoyancy

Chatoyancy, or the cat's eye effect, is a reflection which appears as a single bright band of light across the surface of certain gemstones, when they are cut as cabochons in a certain orientation. Again, chatoyancy is caused by reflection from oriented, long inclusions, when the inclusions are all parallel to one direction.

Gemstones will show a chatoyant reflection when:

(a) The inclusions are long ('needle-shaped');

(b) The inclusions are in parallel arrangement;

(c) The inclusions are sufficiently abundant;

(d) The gemstone is cut in such a way that the top is curved and the base is parallel to the direction in which the inclusions lie.

These inclusions may be either needles or fibres of other mineral substances, or they may be tube-like cavities. To reveal chatoyancy, the gemstone must be cabochon cut.

One variety of Chrysoberyl is even named Chatoyant. Some other gemstones with chatoyant varieties are; Quartz (including Tiger's Eye), Alexandrite, Tourmaline and Beryl. These should not be described simply as cat's eye, but as Quartz Cat's Eye, Tourmaline Cat's Eye and so on.

Alexandrite is a very rare gemstone that under different light sources will demonstrate different hues

Colour change effect

Colour change gems are gems that appear to change their colour when viewed under two different sources of light. It is important to understand that it is actually not the Gem that changes colour, but the way the brain interprets the signal that it receives. Two of the most famous gems that feature this effect are Alexandrite and colour change Garnet.

The sensation of colour change in gems therefore depends upon certain basic requirements:

1. A source of white light
2. Suitable modification to this light
3. The eye and brain to perceive and interpret the light

The change in body colours are caused by the removal, by the gem material, of certain wavelengths of visible light from the white light. The remaining light waves leaving the gemstone are added together and interpreted by the brain as a single colour.

The light which we see mostly appears to be white. The human brain perceives it as a single colour. However, we know through science that white light is made up of the individual colours of the spectrum, its components are combinations of Red, Orange, Yellow, Green, Blue and Violet light.

Lights from different sources have different combinations or balances of these component colours. For example, pure, bright sunlight, has very strong blue components. Light from electric lightbulbs (Tungsten light) seems, to our eyes, to be similar to sunlight but is actually far richer in red wavelengths.

Colour change Garnet is both beautiful and rare

GEM CRYSTAL PROPERTIES

Gems that absorb different light sources and then display different results are referred to as "colour change" gems

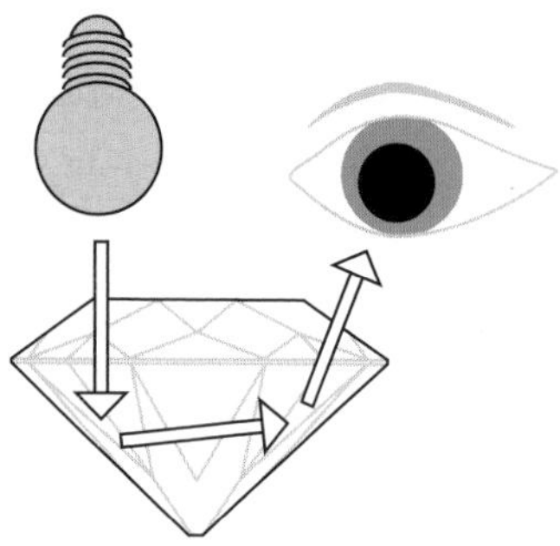

The lightbulb has more red waves than light from the sun

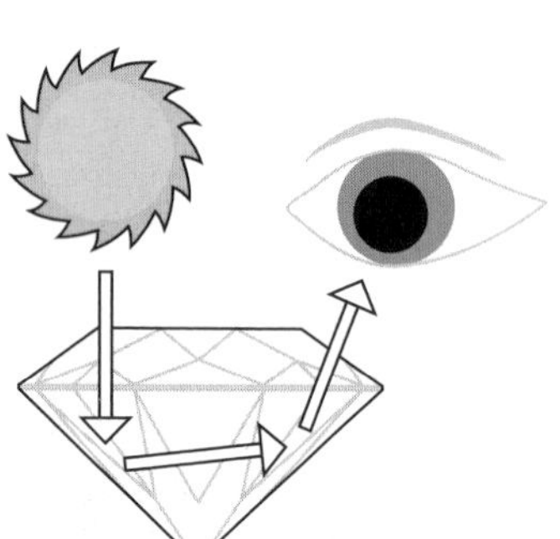

Sunlight features more blue waves.

Exactly how is the colour change effect caused?

When incident light enters a gemstone, it is usually white light. As the light passes through the stone, the gem absorbs some of the component colours of the spectrum. The resulting mixture of light that is 'transmitted' to the human eye has been modified by the gem. The remaining mixture of wavelengths is 'added up' by the brain to perceive a single colour.

This absorption of certain colours, or wavelengths, is called the 'selective absorption of light'. This selective absorption of light wavelengths is always consistent for an individual gemstone. It is this consistency to absorb specific wavelengths that causes our perception of the colour change effect when viewing an item under two different light sources.

The quality and value of a colour change gem is judged by:

1. The strength of the colour change seen
2. The distinctiveness and attractiveness of its colour under sunlight
3. The distinctiveness and attractiveness of its colour under Tungsten Light
4. Clarity
5. Quality of the cut
6. The gem's size and carat weight
7. The gem's rarity in relation to its quality

Double refraction

Double Refraction is an optical "doubling" effect possessed by some gemstones. Gemstones that show double refraction are known as anisotropic gemstones. In these gems we see a "twin" image of features in the gem.

Double refraction is not valuable as an optical property to the jeweller or to the consumer – it largely goes unnoticed. However to the gem dealer and gemologist, double refraction is useful as an aid to identification.

Its two most useful applications are:

1. The distinguishing of Diamond from Moissanite – a very convincing Diamond simulant that shows distinct double refraction while Diamond does not.
2. The immediate identification of Zircon from other gems. Zircon has very strong and noticeable double refraction.

Double refraction has one very unusual side effect that greatly intrigued early man, and, indeed, today some people still find fascinating - pleochroism.

The back facets of Moissanite. Clearly visible is the doubling of the facet lines, a feature that can never be seen in a Diamond

The back facets of a Diamond. No doubling of the facet lines is ever visible

Pleochroism

Atoms in some gemstones (only anisotropic), are arranged in such a manner that light rays are split into two separate components. These two rays possess slightly different colours to each other. The effect to the eye is that a gem exhibits different colour tones when viewed from different angles. This property is known as 'pleochroism'.

Put simply pleochroism is a body colour effect, whereby different body colours are seen in different directions of the gemstone's body.

Examples of strongly pleochroic stones are Iolite, Tanolite™, Tanzanite and Tourmaline.

Many gemstones are pleochroic, but the two component colours seen by the eyes are so similar that we tend not to think of them as being pleochroic even though they are.

Examples of weak to medium pleochroic stones are Ruby, Sapphire, Emerald and Chrysoberyl.

Some gemstones, due to their crystal structures, do not possess any pleochroism at all. This lack of pleochroism is extremely useful when making diagnostic tests on some gems. For example Ruby and Red Spinel share many similar characteristics and often the only way of distinguishing between the two are by pleochroic tests.

Notable examples of non-pleochroic stones are Spinels, Garnets and Diamonds.

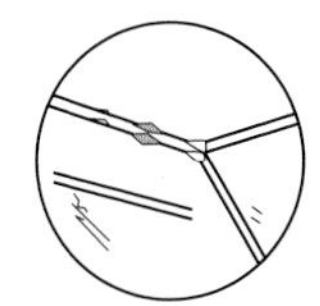

'Doubled" facet edges and scratches seen through the gemstone

The above Tanzanite demonstrates strong pleochroism

FIRE, LUSTRE & BRILLIANCE

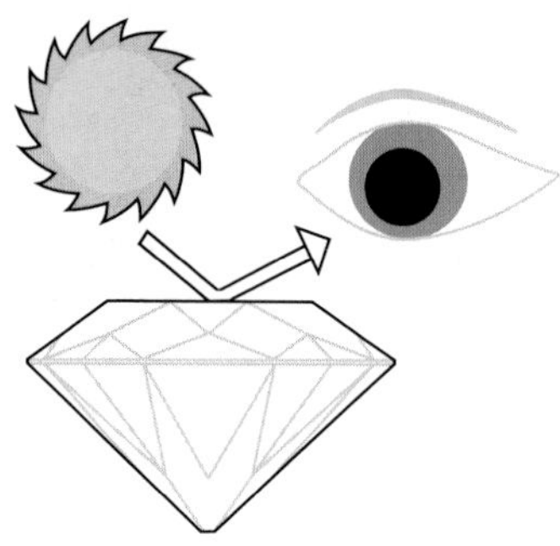

Lustre is the surface reflection of light

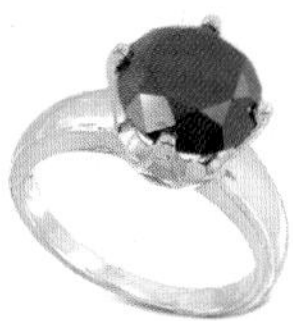

Black Diamonds do not display internal reflections, however, their external lustre is often stronger than white Diamonds

In these earrings featuring both black and white Diamonds, it is the black Diamonds that show stronger lustre. Circled above is not a White Diamond but a high lustre Black Diamond

Fire, lustre, brilliance and iridescence

These often-used terms to describe the visual appearance of the interaction between light and a gem are often misunderstood and even misused by some in the industry.

Put simply, reflection is the return by a surface of some of the light that falls upon that surface. Reflection from gem materials is never perfect. It depends upon the composition and condition of the reflecting surface.

Reflection in gemstones is divided into two categories

	Effects observed
1. External reflection	Lustre
2. Internal reflection	Brilliance Dispersion (fire) Iridescence Asterism & chatoyancy (See page 153)

Lustre

Lustre, defined by both gemology and most dictionaries, is a "surface reflection effect". It is the amount of light that is reflected from a material's surface. The word "lustre" quantifies the reflective power of a material.

If nearly all of the light that falls upon a surface is reflected, resulting in a very bright reflection, the gem is said to have a "high lustre". It is similar to the reflection of the sun off a mirror.

If much of the light is absorbed by the material, resulting in a dull reflection, the material is said to have a "poor lustre". For example a brick would be said to have poor lustre.

The following terms are commonly used to describe the lustre of various gem materials:

Adamantine

Very bright, reflective, almost metallic lustre, as displayed by Diamond.

Sub-adamantine

Bright lustre, often from gemstones having high refractive indices such as Zircon, Corundum and Demantoid Garnet.

Vitreous

The lustre seen in polished glass, and in most transparent gemstones whose refractive indices fall within the middle range of values, for example Emerald and Tourmaline.

Resinous

Certain gem materials that are soft and have low refractive indices, like Amber, have a resinous lustre.

Silky

Some fibrous minerals such as Gypsum and Malachite have a silky lustre.

Metallic

This is the very high lustre shown by metals such as gold and silver, and by gem materials such as polished Hematite and Pyrite.

Pearly

Pearls are composed of crystalline layers from which light is reflected at and near the surface.

Brilliance

Brilliance is a combined internal and external reflection effect. Certain cutting angles allows the light to pass straight through the gem or to be deviated to the side. Accurate cutting to optimum angles will allow light to travel back towards the viewer when looking directly into the table facet.

Gems having low refractive indices (e.g. Quartz, Beryl, Iolite) are not usually cut to show maximum brilliance: a very steep pavilion (base) would be required to cause total internal reflection. Such gemstones require deep settings.

Demantoid Garnet demonstrates bright lustre

Malachite has a silky lustre

Amber has a resinous lustre

FIRE, LUSTRE & BRILLIANCE

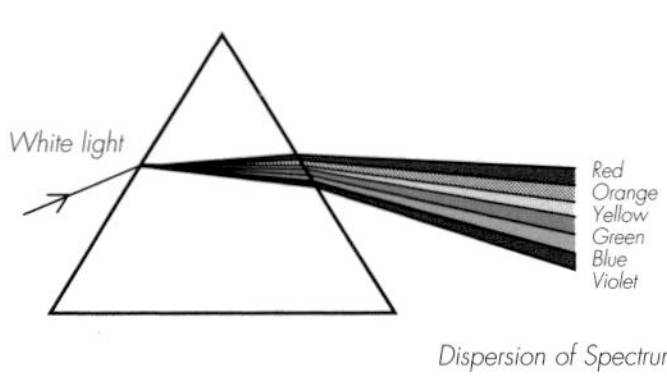

Dispersion of Spectrum

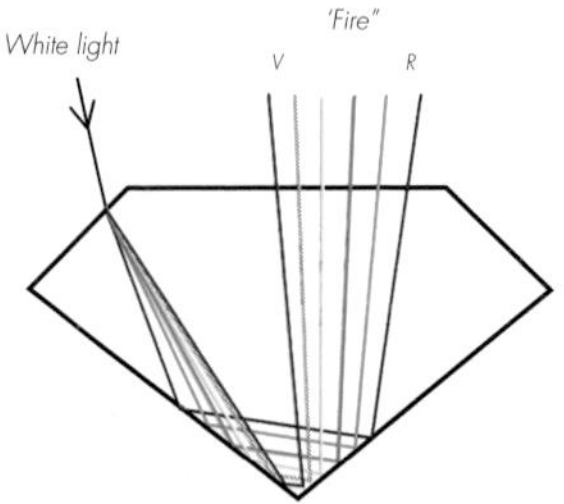

When a gem disperses different colours it is said to have "fire"

Opals often show an incredible amount of iridescence

Pearls have the ability to show a delightfully soft iridescence that provides an extra dimension to this gem of the sea

It is important to note that not all gems have the same optimal cut. Although it is true than many gems demonstrate optimal brilliance when cut to the same proportions as a perfectly "Round Brilliant Cut Diamond", other gem types benefit from either deeper or shallower pavilions. Optimising the cut (faceting) for each gem type is an art in itself. Gems that are not cut correctly, either through a lack of experience or due to the gemcutter aiming to maximise the carat weight, rather than extract maximum beauty, will mean that the gem will not display its optimum brilliance.

Fire (the dispersion of light)

As light passes from one medium to another its individual colours or wavelengths are bent as they enter the new optical medium. Different wavelengths or colours are bent by different amounts.

The resulting effect to the eye is that the light no longer appears to be white, but appears as separate colours. As you move your head you see the colours change – this effect is known as "fire". Diamonds and Zircons are just two examples of gems that normally offer great fire. It is a desirable property and adds both beauty and value to a gemstone when it is present.

Iridescence

An important internal reflection effect caused by structural features is iridescence. Iridescence (play of colour) is a single colour, or a series of colours, produced by lightwaves suffering interference due to structural features or defects. Put simply, iridescence is a colour effect seen when light waves suffer interference, so that some colours are removed and others enhanced.

Some gemstones have a propensity to show different colours of iridescence:

Iridescence (all colours)	Opal
Iridescence (blue white)	Moonstone
Iridescence (very soft)	Pearl

MINING TECHNIQUES

Steve Ashton, who is a TV Presenter on Gems TV in the UK, has written the following section on mining techniques. To gain a better understanding of how gems are formed and then mined, all Presenters on Gems TV have visited at least one gem mine on foreign soil.

In 2005, several of the UK Presenters spent six weeks travelling the globe, visiting nine different countries and dozens of different villages and mines to bring back some stunning video footage. Here, Steve explains the basics of mining for gems.

Generally speaking, the gemstones you will see every day on Gems TV are obtained from mother nature's treasure chest in one of two ways;

a) Host rock mining

b) Alluvial mining

a) Host rock mining

Mineral deposits can be found in different types of locations such as in underground caves (like Moonstone) inside mountains (like Tanzanite and Peridot) or embedded in other elements like Kimberlite (such as Diamonds) in the ground.

Got a craving for caving?

Some gemstones, such as Moonstone, can be harvested directly from underground caves. In the case of Moonstone from Tamil Nadu in Southern India, miners source this gem from mines and limestone caves spread out over a wide area near the village of Kangayam. Here the miners use Moonstone's characteristic shimmer or sheen to their best advantage. Shining flashlights on pegmatite feldspar veins, the illumination of light bounced back from iridescent Moonstone crystals quickly betrays their presence. The typical mining processes for collecting gems from these formations are similar to those used in ancient times - the pick axe and elbow grease.

Gems TV presenter filming at an alluvial mine

This boring technique is used in several countries to manually drill into the soil to hunt for gems

Steve Ashton sent underground in search of Moonstone

Environmentally friendly mining in Thailand

MINING TECHNIQUES

Steve Bennett meets a mine owner in Thailand

Gems TV presenter Matt McNamara shows a Sapphire mine returned to it's original beauty

Our team of buyers and presenters spend a lot of time in Tanzania

A Madagascan windlass mine from which several different gems were recovered

Mine every mountain......

Some of the most beautiful gems that you see on Gems TV come from digging into the side of a hill or mountain. Tanzanite is mined in this way. In the shadows of Mount Kilimanjaro in Northern Tanzania lie the Merelani foothills. Tanzanite is found in metamorphic rocks (these are rocks which have undergone a change in texture or composition as the result of heat and/or pressure) that belong to the Great Rift Valley.

Running at an angle of 41° from the bowels of the Earth to the surface, the deposit line (or strike zone) periodically folds over itself, creating richly coloured and concentrated pockets of Tanzanite.

To get to the Tanzanite, an 'adit' is dug. This is an opening driven horizontally into the side of a mountain or hill for providing access to a mineral deposit.

Pipe mining

The mining of Diamonds can be used to describe the host rock principle very well.

Diamonds are mainly found in an area known as a primary deposit and occur near a 'pipe'. A pipe is a volcanic pathway that connects the earth's deep mantle to its surface. Diamonds are condensed carbon that succumb to extreme pressure and heat to form. They are carried upwards in the pipes amongst magma in volcanic eruptions. Because of the force of the eruption, the Diamond spends enough time to form but not long enough to burn up. The soil that surrounds these volcanic pipes comes in two distinct types, Kimberlite and Lamproite.

Since these eruptions occur mainly on a large scale, Diamond mines tend to be quite large. Initially, Kimberlite is dug from the surface of the pipe in rough, open-cast mines (big holes). Once the surface deposit has been exhausted, shafts are dug into the ground at the edge of the pipes and Kimberlite is extracted.

The way to get the diamond out of the 'host rock' is by applying a little bit of science. Because Kimberlite is not very dense and

Diamond is, essentially a 'sieving' process is used (much like the pan mining techniques seen in good Western movies).

At the Cullinan mine in Pretoria, South Africa, they use a 'sticky table', which is a table covered in grease that the Diamond rich Kimberlite stick to because of their density and the Kimberlite that contain no Diamonds, fall away.

When freed by erosion from the Kimberlite, Diamond crystals can be carried along by rivers. Riverbeds are dug away and the river silt is sieved. This technique is called "alluvial mining". "Marine mining" is the exploitation of sandy coastal strata by dredging. Finding Diamonds can thus be the result of large industrial operations, but also of small-scale methods or even manual labour. Diamonds are rare. It is usual that 250 tons of rock, sand and gravel must be processed to yield one carat of Diamond. The annual world production amounts to approximately 100 million cts of which only 20% are of gem quality.

Songea Sapphire Mine

Songea mine owner, Brad Mitchell sieves the washed rough

b) Alluvial mining

Thousands and thousands of years ago, there were many more mountains than we see today. These mountains contained gemstones. Fortunately for gem lovers, Mother Nature did some of the mining hard work for us. Erosion of these "host rocks" meant that gems (such as Sapphires) were washed down into ancient riverbeds or ocean floors.

Much of the Sapphire you see on Gems TV is alluvially mined.

Typically, a miner will dig using either hand tools (on a small scale mine) or heavy industrial machinery. The rock is taken to the washing process. This is exactly how it sounds. The loose mud will be blasted with water to get rid of the debris, leaving the small gems in the 'wash'. This wash is then trawled through and rough gemstone material is found.

It is an incredibly laborious and time consuming process that can from day to day yield very little.

Returning water to the river bed after mining in Songea

MINING TECHNIQUES

Sieving the washed gemstones

Mining for gems in Songea

Understandably, some of the mines that we visit are so secretive about their location that we can't always reveal their whereabouts

Songea Sapphire Mine where work starts at sunrise

It is extremely rare for miners to find an abundance of gem quality stones in any one day.

History

The oldest known mine in the archeological record is the "Lion Cave" in Swaziland. At this site, which has a radiocarbon age of 43,000 years, men and women mined for the iron-containing mineral Hematite, which they presumably ground to produce the red pigment, ochre.

Sites of a similar age were found in the Netherlands and Hungary and may have been worked for flint for weapons and tools.

Another early mining operation was the Turquoise mine operated by the ancient Egyptians at Wady Maghareh on the Sinai Peninsula. Turquoise was also mined in pre-Columbian America in the Cerillos Mining District in New Mexico, where a mass of rock 200ft in depth and 300ft in width was removed with stone tools; the mine dump covers 20 acres.

Environmental mining

Gems TV strongly believes in only working with environmentally friendly mine owners.

For example, in Songea, in the Ruvuma river region of Southern Tanzania, the mine owner, Brad Mitchell, suffers from freelance miners digging on his mine. (Some refer to them as poachers). They destroy trees and excavate dozens of holes every day in search of the wonderful Songea Sapphire. It is a condition of his license that he leaves the area as he found it. Brad ensures every hole is filled, more trees are planted that are dug and that the landscape is left even better than when he found it. This is the kind of person that Gems TV deals with.

This is just one example of the measures that many mine owners go to to ensure the environment is cared for. In the Bang Ka Ja mine in Thailand, the story is the same and, all over the world, Gems TV works with mines that have a strict environment policy.

Many countries ensure conditions such as this are adhered to, some sadly do not.

FACETING & GEM CUTS

Most gems set in jewellery today will be cut and faceted to some degree (some refer to it as "gem fashioning").

Although gems have been worn, collected and treasured for thousands of years, due to primitive cutting techniques, prior to the 1400s they were not faceted as they are today. When you hear stories about Cleopatra's Emeralds, they would not have been beautifully faceted and, at best, would have been cut into something resembling a cabochon.

It was not until the late 1400s that jewellers began to cut gems with a symmetrical arrangement of facets. The art was not actually perfected until the early 1900s when the first Diamond rotary saw was introduced. Today's modern "Brilliant Round Cut", used in both Diamonds and coloured gems, was first introduced around 1915.

To maximise the beauty of a natural gemstone, it is normally skillfully faceted. As no two pieces of rough (the raw mineral material) are identical, most cutting and faceting of natural gemstones is done by hand.

Although all gems are cut to be viewed from the window (the top of the gem), taking a look at a side profile will provide you with a better understanding of how gems react to light. If the Pavilion is too deep, then light will get trapped inside the gem and once again it will not be bought to life.

Although all gems vary in their optimum shape, understanding the optimum cut for a diamond, will provide you with a good grounding.

In the gems and jewellery market place today, there is a widening range in the quality of gemstone cutting. This is not the result of a global decrease in the skills of gem cutters, but of many jewellery manufacturers opting to compromise the beauty of a gem, in order to maximise the carat weight.

This practice is more common with more expensive gemstones such as Emeralds, Alexandrites, Rubies, Tanzanites and Sapphires. In these instances, many gemstone cutters prefer

Early gems were set almost as they came out of the ground. In the late 1800's gems were cut as cabochons

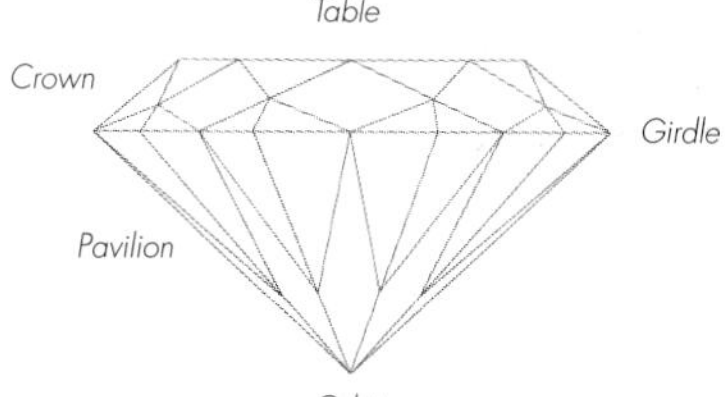

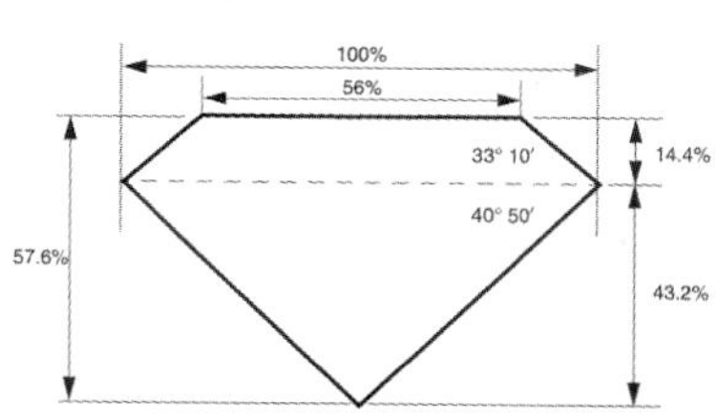

The above dimensions are the normal measurements for a brilliant round cut Diamond

FACETING & GEM CUTS

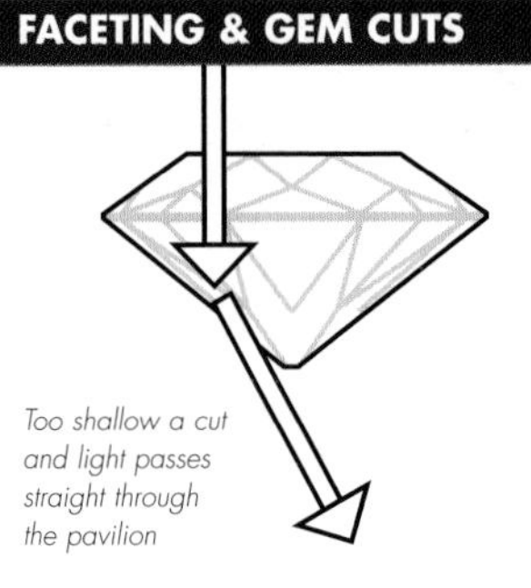
Too shallow a cut and light passes straight through the pavilion

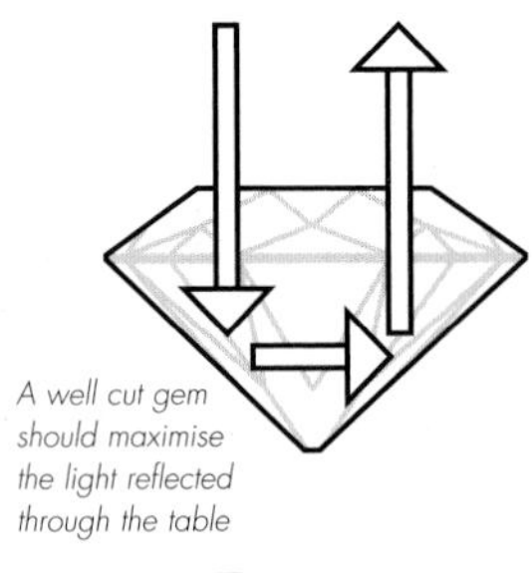
A well cut gem should maximise the light reflected through the table

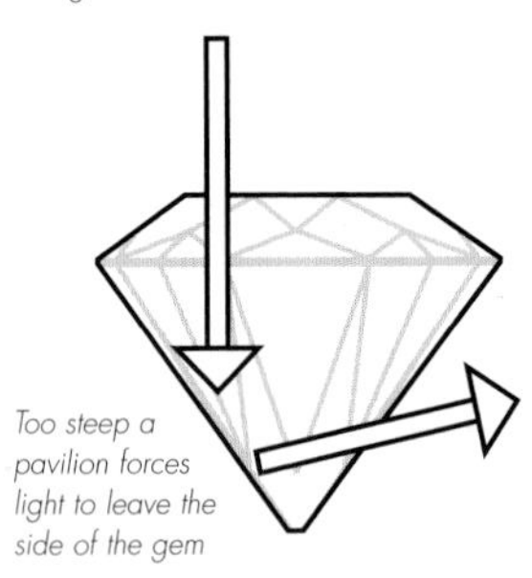
Too steep a pavilion forces light to leave the side of the gem

Opal in its natural rough state before any cuts are made

to ensure the piece maximises its carat weight, rather than cut the gem for optimal beauty.

For less expensive gemstones such as Amethyst, Quartz and Citrine, nearly all craftspeople will search for the optimum cut and not worry about marginally reducing the overall carat weight.

At Gems TV however, our goal is to always bring out the very best of the gem. If this means that the gem weight is 98 points, then so be it.

Our Authenticity Cards shipped with every order will always give you the guaranteed minimum carat weight (page 188).

The importance of fashioning

When we talk about the 4 Cs it is often the "Cut" that is given the least importance. At Gems TV, we believe that when it comes to coloured gemstones, the quality of the cut is crucial.

It is also important to point out that the value of a gem can vary dramatically depending on the quality of the cut.

That's why we believe in spending a little more time and money on trying to achieve the optimum cut.

The cutting and faceting process

Step 1 - Rough selection

Selecting the rough material before cutting is one of the most important stages in the processing of gemstones. It requires tremendous experience and expertise. Mistakes during selection are not tolerated as this step has a direct effect on the outcome of the finished product (i.e. carat weight, quality etc.).

The rough selector's duty is to separate rough gemstones into two groups; those that require further cutting and those that can be preformed.

The clarity of the rough is carefully inspected using a special light source to determine whether it is necessary to cut the rough into two, three or more pieces to obtain the best clarity.

Step 2 - Sliding

Sliding, also referred to as cutting, is one of the most crucial stages (if not the most crucial) in the processing of gemstones, as it will ultimately determine the size and colour of the finished product.

Once the rough is selected, the gem slider will determine how to cut, where to cut, and how many pieces to cut, in order to produce the highest yield percentage. If the rough is cut incorrectly, its colour maybe diminished, relegating an exceptional gem to the ordinary.

Gems TV's air conditioned and natural light cutting rooms are very different to the working conditions witnessed at some independent cutting houses

Step 3 - Preforming

Once the rough has been carefully cut, preforming commences. This process requires tremendous experience and concentration. Preformers carry a great responsibility, as they must determine the most suitable shape for each gemstone.

Preformers always bear in mind the weight of the finished product, as they are also responsible for trying to maintain each gem's weight during the process. In many cases, a qualified selector also assists in determining the shape of a gemstone during the preforming process.

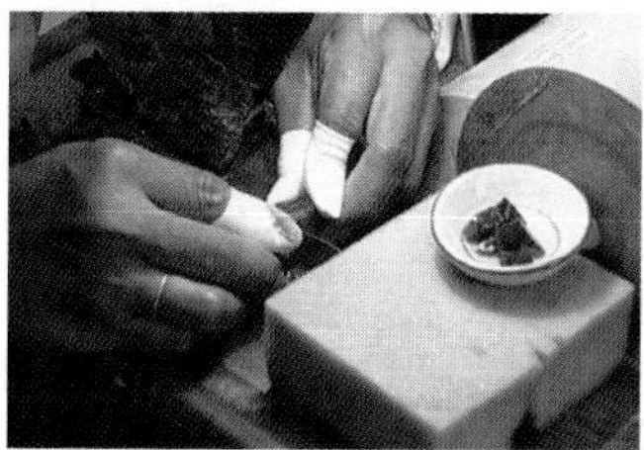

A Gems TV cutter preparing the initial cut on Amethyst

Step 4 - Shaping

The next stage is called shaping. While not all of the preformed gems go through this process, many are shaped to obtain a more accurate presentation and size. The shaper uses a special type of heat activated resin to affix the preformed gemstone onto a metal rod, commonly called a "dob stick". The shaper then delicately applies the gemstone to the shaping wheel.

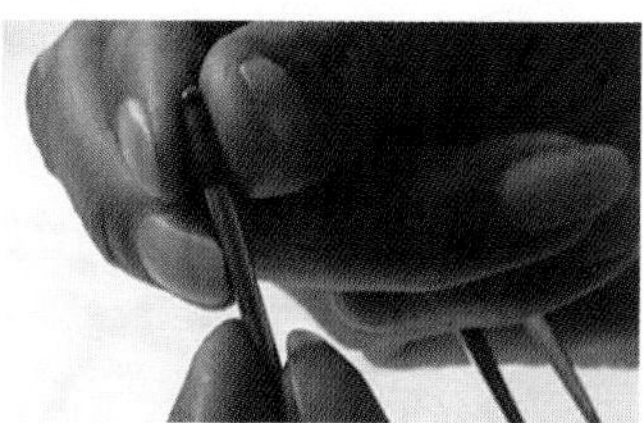

The rough cut gem is fastened to a "Dob Stick" in order to be faceted

Due to the immense precision required by this process, the shaper is usually a very experienced preformer. At the Gems TV Workshop in Chanthaburi, all craftspeople must be over the age of 21 and have had a minimum of three years previous experience in the industry.

Over 50 facets will be added to this gem all by hand

FACETING & GEM CUTS

The surface of the wheel is covered in Diamond dust to finish the faceting process

Gems TV presenter Lynn Garnett with Gems TV's highly skilled gem selectors who sort the faceted gems

Round brilliant cut

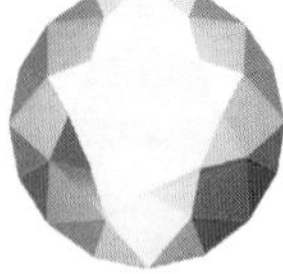

View from table

View from side

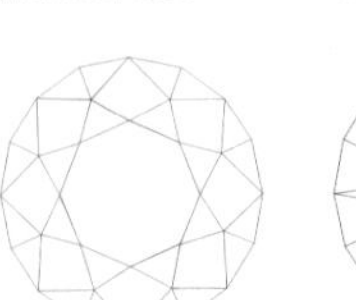

View from table

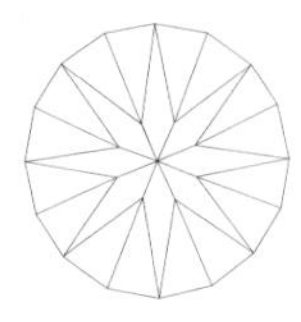

View from culet

Step 5 - Polishing

The final step in the processing of gemstones is known as polishing. Once gemstones have reached their ideal sizes and shapes, they are taken to the polishing wheel where the polisher gives them the final touch, revealing their hidden lustre.

Step 6 - Clarity & quality selection

Before being set in jewellery, qualified professionals carefully examine each gem, separating them according to their clarity, colour, cut and carat weight.

With your satisfaction as our highest priority, Gems TV exerts tremendous effort in ensuring that only the highest quality gems reach our customers. Anything that is not suitable to be set in our jewellery is then sold on to the gem trade.

Cutting styles

Unlike Diamonds, coloured gems possess variable optical properties and are not cut to a uniform ideal. A well-cut coloured gem exhibits even colour, an acceptable number of inclusions, good brilliance and shows the majority of carat weight when viewed from the top (or table).

Broadly, the styles of gem cutting can be divided into faceted gems (gems with geometrically shaped flat polished faces) and non-faceted gems (those gems that do not have geometrically shaped flat polished faces such as cabochons).

Here are the most common cutting styles in the industry that are applied to coloured gemstones. These cuts may be altered or modified by the craftsman who is fashioning the gem. As a general rule, these established styles are only altered to maximise the beauty of a gem and not to maximise the carat weight.

Although some organisations are now starting to use computer aided design (CAD) programs and lasers to cut gems, when it comes to fashioning gems, we still believe in doing things the traditional way. Over the years the jewellery trade have standardised its terminology. When you hear terms such as pear cut, round cut, marquise cut, they normally refer to the shape of the visible facets when the gem is viewed face up.

Round cut

Mostly used for Diamonds, the Diamond Cut or Round Brilliant cut is becoming increasingly used in the coloured gem industry too. It displays maximum brilliance and fire and typically most facets are triangular.

Square cut

A primitive version of the square cut has been used by the industry since the 16th Century and the modern princess cut is a variation of the square. The princess cut is increasingly finding favour amongst consumers and manufacturers alike; its brilliance and light return is far greater than that of the ordinary square cut. The negative point is that it carries slightly less weight in its pavilion than the more traditional, but less brilliant square.

Often a square cut will feature facets arranged in steps running from the girdle up to the table, this is where the phrase "Step Cut" originates. When the four corners of an oblong gem are removed, the cut is referred to as an Emerald Cut, as historically this style of fashioning has been regularly used when faceting Emeralds. Slight variations on the Emerald Cut are the "Radiant Cut" and the "Octagon Cut".

Mixed cut

Round Mixed Cut gems feature both Square Step facets and Round Cut facets. As its brilliance cannot be compared to that of a diamond cut, it is very rarely seen on gem types such as Diamonds. Mixed cuts are mainly used for gems with less brilliance and fire as they are able to hold more carat weight in the pavilion of the gem than the diamond cut.

Princess cut

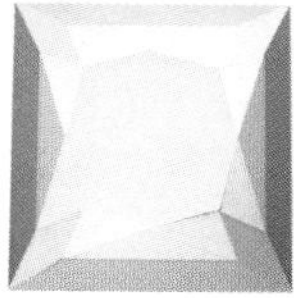

View from table

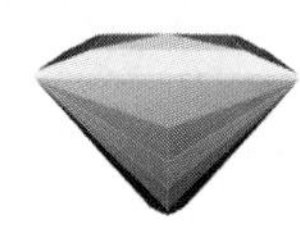

View from side

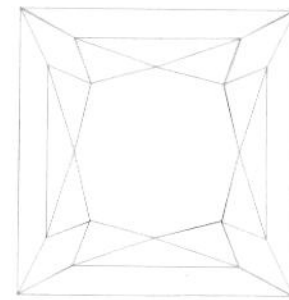

View from table

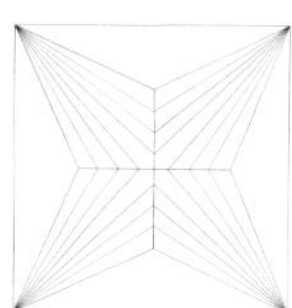

View from culet

Emerald cut

View from table

View from side

View from table

View from culet

Baguette cut

View from table

View from side

View from table

View from culet

FACETING & GEM CUTS

A Rhodolite Garnet uniquely fancy cut to emulate the ace of clubs

Trilliant cut

Round cabochon cut

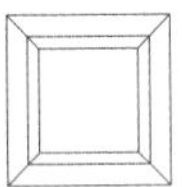

Square cut

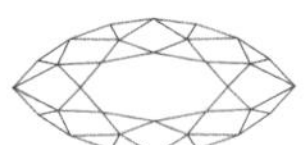

Marquise cut

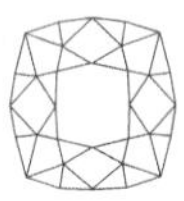

Antique cushion cut

Heart cut

Briolette cut

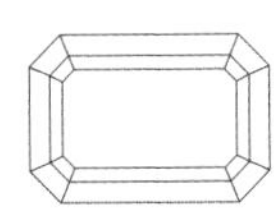

Octagon cut

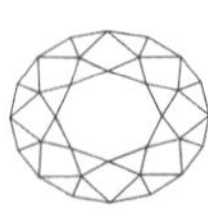

Oval cut

Pear cut

This Spinel gold ring features uncut gems

Fancy cuts

For those who want something really different, recent advances in cutting methods have produced a breathtaking range of innovative new shapes such as cloverleaves, stars, triangles, kites, etc. The important fact to remember is this ever-widening choice of shapes and designs are being created to suit our rapidly growing customer-base of individual collectors, all of whom have their own preference in styles and tastes. The magic of nature and the artistry of the cutter combine to make each design a unique masterpiece.

Tumbling

An alternative to faceting a gem, is tumbling. Tumbled gems can often be found in necklaces and bracelets. Just like pebbles that you find on a beach, some gems are tumbled by Mother Nature. Others are placed into a barrel with water and abrasives and are rotated. Tumbling rough material is obviously less labour intensive than faceting and therefore when manufacturers design jewellery with a big look, they will often choose to tumble the gems.

Uncut gems

Occasionally gems are not cut, faceted or tumbled but set into jewellery literally as they came out of the ground. Although rarely used, this abstract freeform can often produce some beautiful pieces and, because there is no wastage, it yields the maximum value from the natural gem.

Cabochon

One of the oldest forms of fashioning a gem, cabochon cuts are used today primarily for opaque gemstones such as Jasper, Opal, Chalcedony, Jade and Turquoise. Cabochons have a round or oval outline when viewed from the top and, when viewed from the side profile, are domed. This style of fashioning is also used when the gem features optical effects such as chatoyancy (cat's eye) or asterism (star effect). To provide optimum lustre, the gem should not be polished on the flat underside.

Gold

Long considered the most precious of metals, gold is deeply woven into the very fabric of human culture. It captures our imagination and has inspired numerous legends and myths throughout the course of history. Gold has been treasured, hoarded, coveted and lavishly bestowed upon people, temples and objects of worship.

Responsible for creating global currencies, starting wars, toppling empires, causing mass migrations and more, gold has helped shape the course of human history - it is a metal that we are inextricably bound to.

Untarnishable and un-corrodible, it is the most malleable of metals, yet remains miraculously strong. While its rich lustre has long influenced the affairs of state and religion, its primary use remains within the realms of personal adornment.

Frequently featuring as an integral part of antique and modern jewellery's numerous different forms, purchasers should be aware of what gold varieties are on offer and why. The following will shed some light on this ancient metal's application in today's marketplace.

Gems TV presenter Scott Worsfold holding over a kilo of pure gold at our Design Centre and Workshops in Thailand

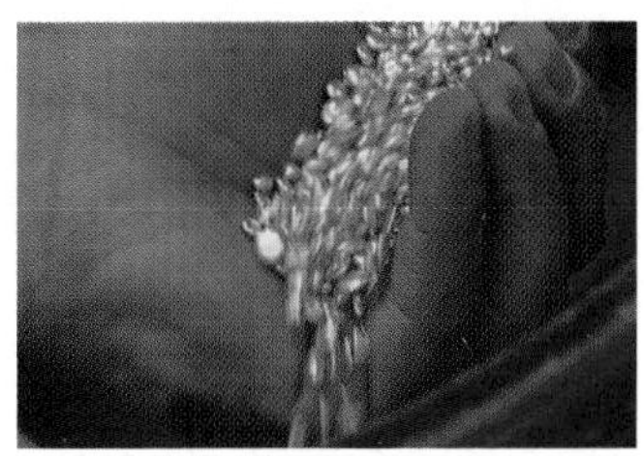

Gold nuggets being mixed with other alloys to produce 9k gold

Gold purity

Pure gold is relatively soft and, as a consequence, has durability problems. Ornate pieces of jewellery can be bent, and expensive gemstones can be lost from their settings. This unacceptable tendency of pure gold has largely given rise to the modern gold we find in the jewellers' window today.

Virtually all gold featured in jewellery today is alloyed with secondary metals that enhance its everyday durability. These gold alloys are so frequent, that, in many countries many people find the colour of pure gold peculiar!

However, not all gold purities are the same. The different purities of gold alloys used by jewellers give consumers varying options regarding gold colour, affordability and durability.

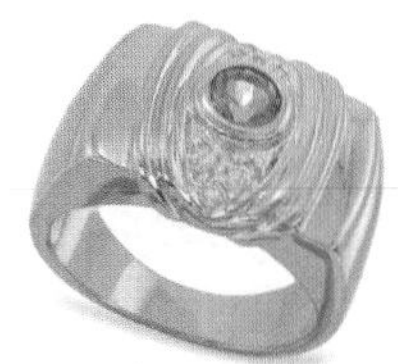

A gent's ring with over 11 grammes of 9k yellow gold

PRECIOUS METALS

Yellow gold is still the most popular in Europe

Palladium is mixed with gold to create white gold

3 Kilos of gold

Above ground stocks of gold in 2004

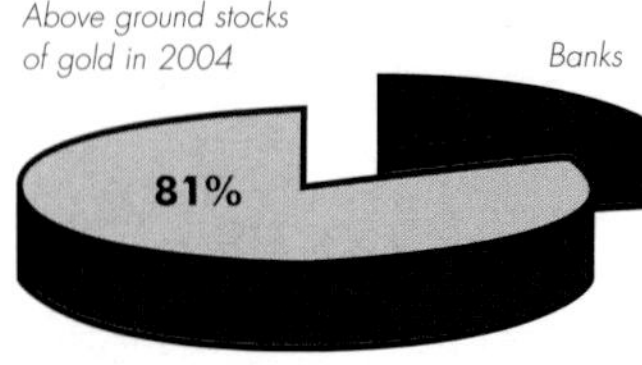

Central banks and supernational organisations hold just under 1/5th of all mined gold

Gold purity is measured in Karats. While the term "Karat" may sound identical to the term "Carat", which is used to measure weight in gemstones, the two terms do not have the same meaning. Karat ratio in gold tells you the percentage or proportion of gold purity. Gold with a higher Karat ratio, is comparatively more expensive gram for gram when compared to gold with lower Karat ratios. Expressed as a ratio of 24 parts, the most frequently seen gold purities are:

22 Karat:	91.6%	Pure Gold
18 Karat:	75%	Pure Gold
14 Karat:	58.5%	Pure Gold
9 Karat:	37.5%	Pure Gold

Gold colours

Gold comes in a number of different colours offering consumers a wide choice when buying this lustrous precious metal:

Yellow gold: The most frequently seen gold type that displays a timeless colour. It is usually alloyed with silver and copper.

White gold: Harder than yellow gold with a bright lustrous white colour, white gold is most commonly alloyed with palladium. Palladium, a rare and expensive precious metal, increases the value of white gold to above that of yellow gold.

Rose gold: Mostly alloyed with copper, this increasingly popular gold type has a striking pink to reddish hue.

Gold sources

Gold is mined in only a handful of countries. In terms of output, the main sources are South Africa, USA, Australia, Canada, China, Russia, Peru and Indonesia.

Gold as an Investment

Due to the popularity of gold, it has been used to both purchase goods and exchanged for goods for thousands of years. Even until the early 1900s, gold reserves formed the basis of the world monetary systems. Even today, a huge proportion of the world's gold, is held in Government Reserves. When you purchase gold jewellery, although you are not guaranteed that you will ever make a profit on your acquisition, you are assured that you have gained something with intrinsic value.

Silver is extremely popular and is mainly used for fashion jewellery

Silver

With a rich history stretching back some 5,000 years, like gold, silver occupies a hallowed place in our collective history. From the age-old Sumerian city of Ur, to the ancient Americas, to Greco-Roman culture and the ancient Far East, silver has been used by nearly all global cultures over the last two millennia.

Sharing much in common with its more glamourous counterpart, gold, silver, too, is most frequently used for personal adornment.

Silver in its rough nugget form

Silver purity

Like gold, pure silver or fine silver is relatively soft and malleable. As a result, painstakingly crafted jewellery and other objects can be easily damaged if created from pure silver. As a consequence, silver is commonly alloyed with secondary metals, usually copper, to create a more durable precious metal.

Sterling Silver is the standard for beautiful high-quality silver jewellery and other objects d'art. It's 92.5% pure silver and is alloyed with secondary metals for added strength and durability. Unlike gold, but like platinum, silver purities are expressed as units of 1,000 parts. The most regularly seen silver purities are:

958: 95.8% Pure Silver, also known as Britannia Silver.

925: 92.5% Pure Silver, also known as Sterling Silver.

British hallmarks for silver

Sterling silver

Britannia silver

Platinum

Sixty times rarer than gold, platinum is only found in a few locations worldwide - Russia's Ural Mountains, South Africa's Merensky Reef,

PRECIOUS METALS

and a few small mines in the USA and Canada. Relatively new to the jewellery market, platinum is fast becoming incredibly popular and is already a bedrock of the contemporary jewellery landscape. Purer, stronger and denser than gold, platinum is considered by many to be the ultimate and most luxurious of all the precious metals.

A platinum engagement and wedding ring designed by Gems TV

Platinum purity

Platinum purity is expressed differently than gold. Instead of expressing purity in ratios of 24 parts, platinum standards are expressed as units of 1,000 parts. The most regular platinum purities seen are:

950:	95%	Pure Platinum
900:	90%	Pure Platinum
850:	85%	Pure Platinum

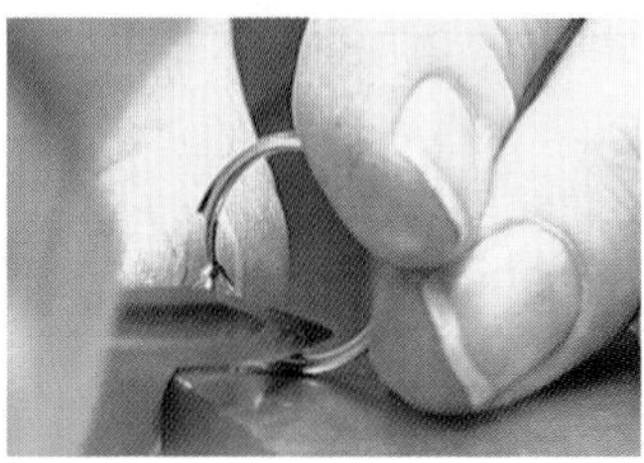

The Assay Office scrape a sample of gold to test for purity

Hallmarking

Hallmarking is used in several countries around the globe to protect the public against fraud and traders against unfair competition.

Introduced in 1327, it represents one of the earliest forms of consumer protection. In the UK, a hallmark consists of three compulsory marks which give you the following information:

- Who presented the jewellery (sponsor or makers mark)
- What is its guaranteed standard of purity
- What Assay Office tested and marked the jewellery

With gold, it is a British legal requirement to hallmark all items that contain over 1 gramme of gold, whereas with silver it is a requirement to hallmark all items containing over 7.78 grammes.

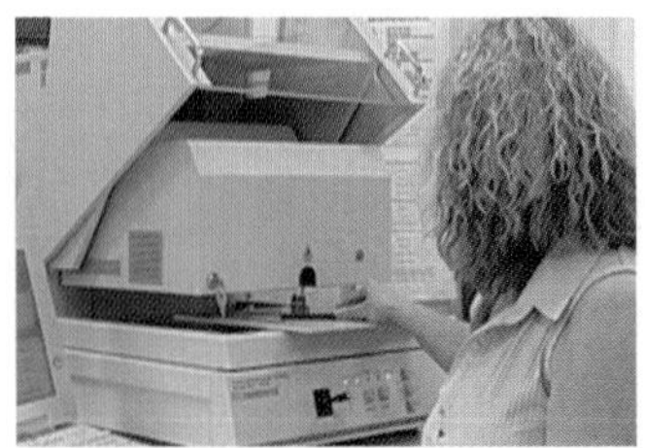

Technology is increasingly being used to back up the historical method of cupellation to confirm gold purity

Another way Gems TV goes just that little bit further in making your jewellery special is in the application of a date symbol at the Assay Office. In the past, it was a legal requirement to add a symbol to the hallmark to show the year that the item was hallmarked. Today, this requirement has been removed. However, Gems TV continues to have the additional mark added to the hallmark. The reason that we do this is that we believe it adds extra value to the piece in years to come.

Imagine the feeling your great grandchildren will have when looking at the hallmark and being able to use the Internet to identify the year the jewellery was marked.

Sponsor or maker

This shows the person or company responsible for sending the jewellery to the Assay Office. The sponsor may be the manufacturer, retailer, importer, etc. In our case you will find the marks "GTV", which shows it is a genuine Gems TV product.

The Assay Office sometimes use lasers

Assay office mark

There are four British Assay Offices, Birmingham (Anchor), Edinburgh (Castle), London (Leopard's Head) and Sheffield (Rose):

Birmingham

Edinburgh

London

Sheffield

Standard marks

These show the standard of fineness, the purity of the precious metal, in parts per thousand.

9 carat

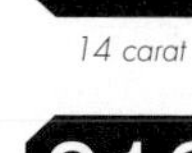

14 carat

18 carat

22 carat

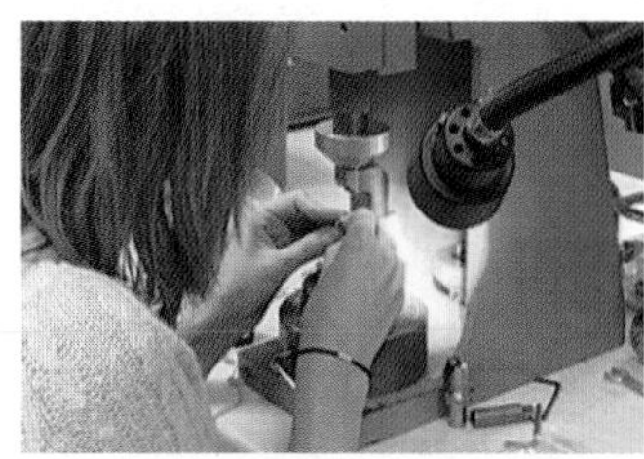

Gems TV jewellery receiving its official stamp

JEWELLERY MAKING

We employ over 1200 dedicated gem fanatics in Thailand

Nearly all designs are drawn by hand and not with computer systems

Head of Business Development Theo van Dort discusses jewellery design with one of our designers in Thailand

It is important to add such details as prong type to the initial design documents

Established in 1998, the Gems TV Design Centre and Creativity Workshops in Chanthaburi Thailand employ over nine hundred and forty master craftsmen and women.

At Gems TV, we believe we have developed a completely new way of conducting business in the jewellery industry. As we cut out all of the middlemen and sell our handcrafted jewellery direct to the consumer, it has meant that we can continue in the tradition of handcrafting jewellery, but on a large scale.

Interestingly, we believe that due to the efficiencies of the way we conduct our business, we can continuously sell our handcrafted designs direct to the public, at prices substantially below those charged for jewellery that travels a convoluted route from the mass making machines to the eventual consumer.

Our design process

Whilst the UK sleeps, our designers in Thailand are constantly researching jewellery and fashion houses from around the world, finding inspiration for the multitude of new designs they produce on a daily basis.

With a rich and varied colour palette, using hand drawing and water colour techniques, the team expertly design beautiful and intricate pieces, to complement the gemstones that have recently arrived at the workshops after being unearthed from Mother Nature.

Not only do we create our own designs, but frequently we will use drawings and concepts sent to us from our customers to form the foundation of a design.

With a target of over one hundred and twenty different designs and combinations to achieve each day, our design centre is always bustling with excitement.

Our approach is also very different to that of almost any other jewellery design house. Rather than design the jewellery first and then hunt down or cut the gems to fit the design, we turn the whole process on its head and start with the gem. This unique approach also helps Gems TV provide such excellent value to its customers.

Gem sorting and colour matching

In the gem sorting room, our diligent team sort and colour match gems for each piece. The art of colour matching requires immense visual concentration and it is an ability that the Managing Director of Gems TV Europe believes is not suitable to the western world. Steve Bennett says "after spending many hours with the gem sorting team, I find it hard to comprehend how other cultures could do such an intense job and derive pleasure from it. Because of the gems history and culture in Chanthaburi, there is an inbuilt fascination with coloured gemstones, which provides the gem sorters with a genuine enjoyment of their job, which, to other cultures would be considered a laborious task. I personally have tried to do it and, to my eyes, the gems looked perfectly matched, however Lin, who was overviewing my work at the time, told me that I had made some very bad judgements and that in certain lighting conditions, the stones would not match. I also learnt that, in a Half Eternity ring, they even make allowances for the fact that the stones at each end of the shoulders are naturally viewed at a different angle, therefore they have to make different selections for each gemstone in order to give a perceived unity of colour to the naked eye when viewed as a whole!"

As Mother Nature does not produce any two gems absolutely identical, it is imperative that the process of colour sorting and matching is taken extremely seriously.

Initially, a batch of gems will be sorted into five different colour bands. Only gems from the same colour grade can be given the same model number. Assume, for example, that out of a batch of 170 faceted Tanzanite's, only 44 are given a colour code "3". Then the "Colour Sorting Manager" will inform the design team of the quantity available and they will, for

Steve Bennett, the Managing Director of Gems TV Europe learning about colour matching

A large batch of gems being colour sorted

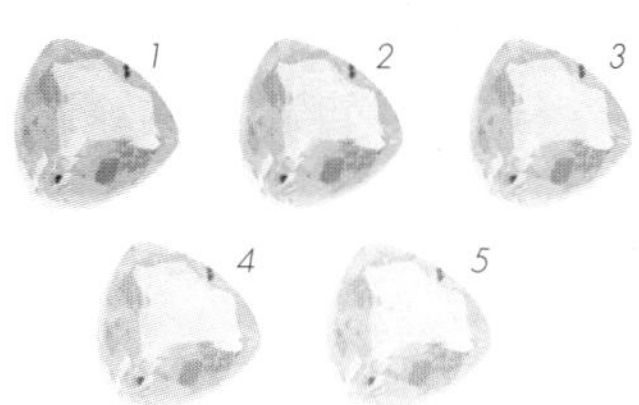

Only gems from one colour band are used in each design

Gems TV presenter Matt McNamara learns how Rubies are colour graded

We still use traditional methods to stretch gold

example, either make 11 rings with 4 gems in each, 22 rings with 2 gems in each or 44 solitaire rings.

If the design team decide to make 11 rings containing 4 gems, they will inform the Colour Sorting Team to further sort the 44 gems into perfectly matching groups of four.

The crafting process

Once the designs have been created and after the gems have been selected and matched, the next task is to craft the precious metal.

For smaller quantities, the craftspeople literally start with an amount of gold and cut, shape, heat and stretch it into the final article. For larger quantities, we make an original master piece and cast the required quantity of pieces from the master and then finish them all by hand.

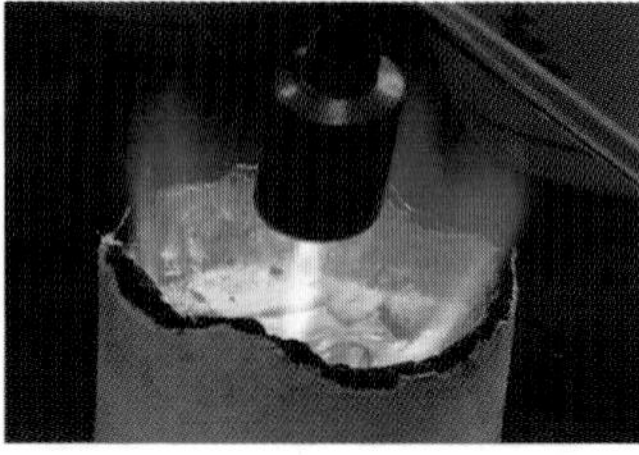

Gold being melted to form a one of a kind masterpiece

Many of the handcrafted pieces start from gold bars or nuggets. The craftspeople are given the correct amount of gold for the design and begin by adding alloys to create 9k, 14k and 18k yellow, white or rose gold. You can imagine with so much gold being consumed everyday, that security measures are very tight.

The first task is to melt the gold to make it easier to craft the first few steps of the design. To do this the craftspeople effectively use a blow torch to heat the precious metal to a temperature of 1064C (1337.59F)

For some designs, rather than starting with nuggets of gold, the craftspeople may start with a length of gold that is already shaped into a round rod. The equipment we use to stretch the gold into the correct thickness is traditional and the skills have been passed on by many generations. Nick Davies, one of the Gems TV presenters, said "the equipment used, with its battered wooden wheel and worn belt, wouldn't look out of place in a Medieval Torture Chamber!"

The body of a ring starting to take shape

Once the gold has been heated and cut into a rough state, the craftspeople start to shape the body of the ring. The art is fascinating to watch and within minutes you see a flat piece of metal being turned into the body of the ring by a craftsman whose only tools are his hammer and his wealth of experience.

A craftsman removes the wax from the rubber mould

Wax mould techniques

For the larger quantities that we create, we use a wax moulding technique to construct the first step of the ring. The master model making workshop comprises of two sections: silver model makers and wax carvers. Their expertise is diverse and includes everything from simple, elegant prong set gemstone jewellery designs to artistically crafted masterpieces. These craftspeople are of critical importance, as their ability to turn a one dimensional drawing into a three dimensional master model is vital in ensuring that the finished jewellery exceeds all expectations. As with the old carpenters adage, measure twice cut once, all our master models must be exactingly precise, as any mistakes at this stage are going to appear in the finished jewellery.

Wax moulds are thoroughly checked before being cast

Wax injection

Once a master mould has been approved, it arrives at the Wax Injection Workshop.

From the wax or silver master mould, a number of rubber moulds are created. These rubber moulds encapsulate the shape of the original master and then wax is injected into the void. Once the wax sets, the rubber mould is removed and you are left with perfect replicas of the original master mould. These replicas are then checked to ensure they are identical to the original, then the required quantity are created and placed on to a wax tree ready for casting.

A tree of wax rings being put into the cylinder

Casting

The wax tree is inserted into a cylinder and then ceramic cement (known as investment) is poured into the cylinder to surround the tree. Once the cement has set, the cylinder is heated until the wax melts and drains from the bottom of the cylinder. The gold or silver is then poured into the cylinder to replace the spaces left by the

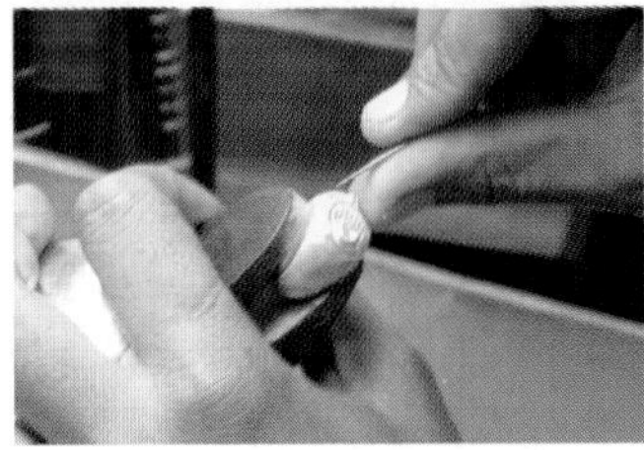

After casting, everything else is done by hand - the rings are carefully prepared for gem setting

Rubies being set into a pendant

The last step before Quality Control is to polish the jewellery

departed wax. This process takes place in a vacuum to ensure that every crevice is filled.

Once the precious metal sets, the cylinder is cracked open and the jewellery is removed from the now gold tree. From this point on, every single process in the creation of the jewellery is done by hand.

Jewellers (pre-finishing)

The jewellers or pre-finishing workshop carefully prepares and assembles the jewellery components ready for gem setting, all the while understanding the finishing needs for each individual design. In the case of bracelet assembly, the components are all assembled by hand (no mass production here). As with all workshops involved in the handcrafting of your jewellery, an embedded quality control team checks every handcrafted piece before approving them for transfer to the next workshop.

Gem setting

Using an array of very traditional tools, the gem setting team are responsible for mounting the gems into the jewellery. This might sound a straightforward task, however a great deal of skill is required to ensure that the precious metal is shaped and modified by hand to securely hold each individual gem. The gem setting workshop employs a team of highly experienced craftsmen and women who, on average, can only set approximately 120 gemstones per day per person. It can take a setter a whole day to set just one bracelet and, if the gems are bezel set, it is not uncommon for the piece to take several days! Different setters specialise in different disciplines. Some are experts in prong setting, while others specialise in channel and bar settings.

Polishing

In the polishing workshop, we ensure that the best shine and finish are achieved whilst essential relevant details of your handcrafted jewellery are maintained. This is done by the careful separation of individual polishing needs.

Quality assurance

The final product approval is done by the quality assurance team and is run by a group of experts with years of experience in the creation of high quality handcrafted jewellery. They ensure that quality standards that exceed your expectations are always met, by working closely with quality control teams embedded in each workshop.

The Gems TV crafting team

Being based in the Gem capital of Chanthaburi, Gems TV is ideally located to recruit some of the most talented jewellery craftspeople in the world.

One of the highest accolades for anybody working in the crafting of jewellery is to participate in the Worlds Skills Competition (Also known as the "Skills Olympics"). Over its 45 year history, the "Skills Olympics", has come to symbolise the pinnacle of excellence in jewellery crafting.

Gems TV jewellery maker, Mr. Maykin Wilaikarn won a Silver Medal for Thailand at the 37th World Skills Jewellery Competition held in St. Gallen, Switzerland, in 2003.

Maykin earned his spot in the World Skills jewellery-making event by edging out over 500 entries in both regional and national competitions. His jewellery-making techniques were learnt from his uncle and are now being developed alongside other Gems TV team members.

Fortunately, Maykin didn't have to face the media interest unprepared, as he was actually the second Gems TV craftsman to win a medal at the World Skills Competition, joining Mr. Ridsin Sre-a-pond, who is one of our Master Mould Makers, who won the Bronze Medal in the same category in Seoul, Korea, 2001.

Every single piece of our handcrafted jewellery is quality controlled before leaving Thailand

After quality control, your Authenticity Certificate is produced

All our high quality handcrafted jewellery is presented in stylish and protective packaging

JEWELLERY SETTINGS

At Gems TV we use a wide variety of beautiful settings

Most jewellery is crafted from individual components. The pieces are often created on the jewellers' bench and then skillfully adjoined with precious metals. The components needed in most types of jewellery are incredibly simple. Even the most expensive Tiffany-style Diamond ring features just three pieces - the band of the ring, the gallery that mounts the claws, and then finally the jewel itself.

With a few peripheral components such as earring-posts, chain, and hinges (often known as "findings") these basic components are used to make everything from solitaire and gem set rings, to earrings, necklaces, pendants and more complex pieces. While the claw setting is the most frequently seen method of setting solitaire gem set rings and Diamonds, there are a variety of other methods also used to set jewels in precious metals.

Claw setting

Claws are the most frequently seen method of setting gems in jewellery. Small precise precious metal claws command a vice-like grip, which bends over the girdle of the gem to ensure its secure and enduring position.

Claw settings are frequently seen because they are relatively simple to work with. Easy to adjust to the size of an individual gemstone, claw settings usually feature anywhere from four to six claws. However, marquise and trilliant cut gems can respectively have just two or three claws at the corners where the points of the jewels are nestled in specialised v-shaped claws.

Claw set

Bezel setting

Securely encircling the entire circumference of the gem, a bezel is a crafted diskette of metal that holds the gemstone by its girdle to the ring. An age-old technique that can appear very contoured and modern, it is labour intensive and must be crafted to precisely circumnavigate the outline of the gem.

A variation of the bezel setting is the flush or gypsy setting. The surface of the ring has a window cut into it that exactly fits the size of the gem. Secured from underneath, the crown of the gem rises from the ring beautifully catching rays of light.

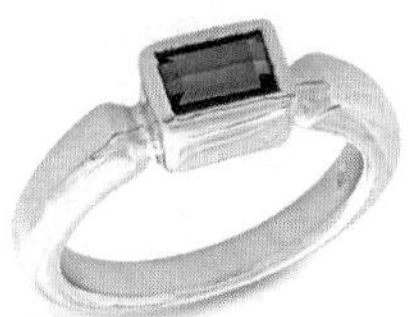

Bezel set

Channel setting

Often seen in eternity bands and tennis bracelets, gemstones are held side-by-side by their girdles between two long tracks of precious metal. When used with square, princess and rectangular shaped jewels, the effect is breathtaking as no metal appears between the jewels - they appear to float in a tightly bejeweled chain within the jewellery.

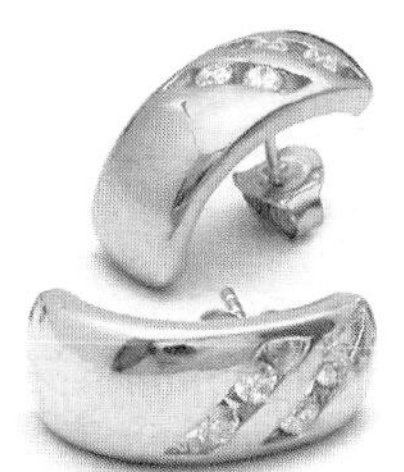

Channel set

Bar setting

An increasingly popular setting style, bar settings features Diamonds or gemstones individually set between short bars that run like a railway track across the ring. Each gem is set between the two small parallel bars and the sides of the gems are left open. This open-sided technique maximises the amount of light entering the gems, which creates superior brilliance and sparkle.

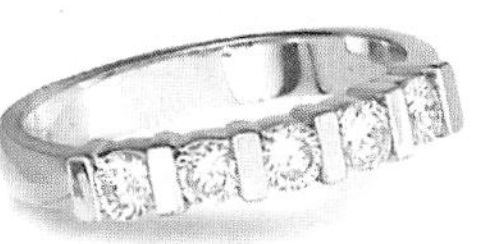

Bar set

Pave setting

Pave setting produces a carpet of brilliance across the entire surface of a piece of jewellery. The surface is encrusted, or quite literally "paved" in Diamonds and gems, and the body of the jewellery is vibrantly brought to life.

Pave setting is often used in conjunction with white gold, which further creates an effect of the whole piece of jewellery being crafted from Diamonds. While also regularly seen in yellow gold, the pave technique is rarely used in platinum. The settings are either created by the use of tiny prongs that hold the jewels on both sides, or are crafted by scooping out small beads of precious metal and replacing them with the jewel.

Pave set

THE GEM SUPPLY CHAIN

A busy gem trading hall full of brokers, agents and dealers

A gem dealer selling gems by their carat weight

The gem supply chain

The supply chain in the coloured gem industry is extremely long – longer than the Diamond supply chain. It is not uncommon for a gemstone to pass through 7 and 10 pairs of hands from the mine to the consumer. By any industry standard, this is an extremely long and inefficient supply chain – although the price keeps going up, other than at the cutting and setting stages, there is no real "value add" being applied to the gem.

On its passage through so many pairs of hands, it is not uncommon for a coloured gemstone to increase in price by up to 1,000%! For example, this means a £200 Tanzanite gemstone from Tanzania may end up selling for £2,000 in the jewellers window and this does not even include the other jewellery components. Once you factor in labour, gold and Diamonds, our Tanzanite that started at £200 could end up retailing in a shop window for a whopping £4,000!

The typical pairs of hands a coloured gemstone will pass through from the mine to consumer are highlighted below:

The supply chain - loose gem	Position sale prices (£ per Carat)
1. Miner	£100
2. Broker	£150
3. Cutters	£225
4. Wholesalers (Thailand)	£375
5. Wholesalers (U.S.A/Europe)	£600
6. Retailer	£700
7. Consumer	£1,000
The final consumer pays 1000%	**£1,000**

At Gems TV, our aim is to remove as many of these stages as possible.

As we buy gems at their original source (or as close to the source as possible) and manufacture and retail our own handcrafted jewellery, we offer prices that cannot be matched.

CARAT WEIGHT EXPLAINED

Carat weight

The weight of a gem is measured in carats (ct). Unfortunately this is easily confused with the measurement for the purity of gold which is also a karat (k). The name "carat" dates back to ancient times, when gems were measured on scales against the "carob bean". The carob was used as they had a very consistent weight.

At the end of the 19th Century, the carat weight measurement was internationally standardised at a fifth of a gram. Gemstones under 1ct are measured in points. A 50 point gemstone can also be referred to as a half a carat and a 25 point can be referred to as a quarter of a carat.

A 2.709 carat "one of a kind" Alexandrite ring sold on Gems TV for £2,497 in September 2005

How does carat weight affect price?

Generally speaking, if you take two gemstones with different carat weights, but with similar cut, clarity and colour, the one with the higher carat weight will be valued higher. However, if the cut has been compromised in order to obtain maximum carat weight, a reduction in beauty might reduce the value of the gem.

With rare gemstones such as Alexandrite, Tanzanite, Ruby, Diamond and Sapphire, a 1ct gemstone in one piece is more valuable than say five 20 point gemstones of the same colour and clarity. Although the combined weight of the five gemstones is still 1ct, the rarity of a singular 1ct gem is much greater, thereby demanding a far higher price.

56 Individual 12 point Alexandrites in a beautiful handcrafted bracelet sold on Gems TV for £897 in September 2005

Take, for example, a 16ct Ruby sold at Sotheby's in New York in October 1988 for a staggering $3,630,000! If pricing was linear, that would make a similar 1ct Ruby worth $226,875!

The only exception where the combined weight of smaller gems might cost more than a singular gem of the same carat weight is where the cost of labour in applying all of facets to the individual gems outweighs the difference in gem price.

If you are buying a gem with a rounded carat weight, make sure that the quality of cut has not been compromised to achieve this rounded number.

TOP 9 TIPS

The sign of quality gemset jewellery

9 Tips to buy gems and jewellery

One of the best ways to ensure that you are getting great value when collecting jewellery is to always purchase from Gems TV!

However, we do appreciate that if you are looking for a particular gemstone that for some reason we temporarily cannot source, you might want to use other jewellers in order to expand your collection. Here are our top nine tips to help you judge the value of your potential purchase.

1. Make sure it is the real thing!

"There is no fraud or deceit in the world which yields greater gain and profit than the counterfeiting gems." (Pliny the Elder in his Historia Naturalis, 1st Century AD).

The fraudulent selling of fake gems and fake gold is unfortunately as widespread today, as it was in the 1st Century AD. Compounding the problem is the introduction of lab generated gems that are very difficult to distinguish from the real thing. There are many books written on the subject and the Internet is becoming a very useful tool in providing more information on identifying the real thing from the impostors.

Watch out for Diamond imitators such as Cubic Zirconia and Moissanite

Take Diamonds for example. We recommend that you only buy Diamond jewellery from reputable jewellers. Be aware that several man made substitutes such as Cubic Zirconia and Moissanite are very difficult to detect with the naked eye. The Gemological Institute of America's website (www.gia.edu) offers good advise on spotting Cubic Zirconia and Moissanite.

2. Colour

A vivid coloured Chrome Diopside ring

Study the colour of the gem and if possible make comparisons to others. While vivid, saturated, deeper colours are generally more highly prized, colour preferences are ultimately up to personal taste. The best colour for any gemstone should be obvious from several feet or even several yards away.

3. Carat & clarity

Larger gems are more highly prized than small ones and gems with fewer and smaller inclusions are generally more highly prized than those with more numerous and larger inclusions.

However, please remember that sometimes inclusions increase the value of a gemstone or are a common natural characteristic.

For example, fine inclusions that cause star or cat's eye effects increase the value of a gem and inclusions in Emeralds (see page 42) are a common feature that show the gem's natural relationship with the Earth.

A 26ct Swiss Blue Topaz which has near perfect clarity

4. Cuts

Well cut gems of good symmetry, attractive design and fine polish are more prized than poorly cut gems. Regrettably, some gemstones, such as Ruby and Emerald, are often poorly cut in order to maximise weight at the expense of their appearance.

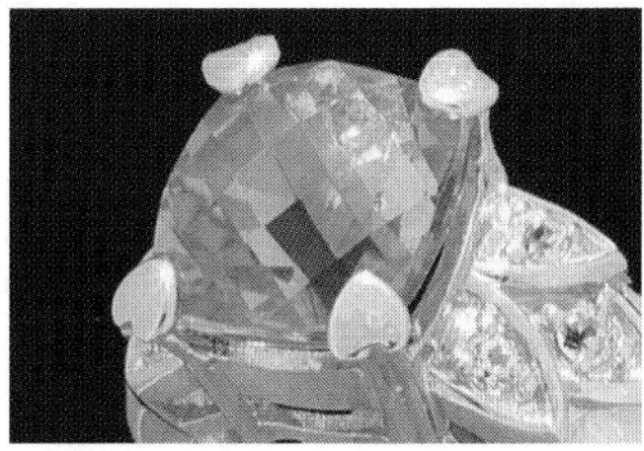

At Gems TV we believe that the quality of the cut is paramount

5. Rarity

Rare gems are more highly prized than more common varieties. However, if the gem is so rare that it is essentially unknown to the general public, its value suffers and it is relegated to the status of a "Collectors' Gem".

Gems such as Bracite, Cildrenite, and Simpsonite are extremely rare, attractive and durable, but don't command prices appropriate to their rarity, because there are currently few people aware or eager to buy them.

Goshenite, whose siblings include the well known Emerald and Aquamarine, is a rare member of the Beryl family

6. Historical connotations

While there are exceptions, gemstones that are rich in history and folklore are generally more prized than those lacking historical connotations.

TOP 9 TIPS

A brass bracelet gold plated and fraudulently sold as 18k gold

7. Is it real gold?

Plated gold is sometimes sold as real gold. If a street vendor offers you gold jewellery at a price that you feel is unbelievable, then it probably is! Remember that seeing 9K or 18K engraved on jewellery does not guarantee that it is real gold. If you are in a country where there is an official government stamp, such as the United Kingdom or Switzerland, then ensure that the correct stamp has been applied (see page 175).

Don't do a Barry! Even our Managing Director's assistant Barry has been caught out when buying gold. While on holiday he was offered a bracelet that was stamped 18k (see picture on the left) but when he had it checked back in the UK, it was found to be gold plated brass.

8. Guaranteeing weight

Check with the jeweller whether the weight of gold and the carat weight of the gems are an average or are guaranteed. If they are only an average, you should ask the salesperson "what is the range". In most countries, respectable jewellers will be aware of the range of tolerances used by their suppliers. If you are unsure about your gram and carat weight, ask the retailer to put into writing what they will guarantee.

CERTIFICATE OF AUTHENTICITY

Item No: 32485
MTGW: 1.406ct
Metal Type: 9K Yellow Gold
Approx Metal Weight: 2.59g
32485-0002 HANDCRAFTED

GOLDEN SAPPHIRE & DIAMOND GOLD EARRINGS

CERTIFICATE OF AUTHENTICITY

Item No: 30307
MTGW: 2.483ct
Metal Type: 9K Yellow Gold
Approx Metal Weight: 2.97g
30307-0010 HANDCRAFTED

GREEN SAPPHIRE GOLD RING

All Gems TV jewellery comes with a minimum total gem weight (MTGW) guarantee

9. Insurance

Don't assume that your jewellery collection is automatically insured by your household policy. It is always wise to take photos and catalogue all of your jewellery. Try and keep all your receipts and get as much written details as possible from the retailer. If your catalogue is a hard copy, make sure you take a photocopy and keep the second copy at a friend's house or as some collectors do, leave a copy with your family lawyer or solicitor. If your catalogue is a soft copy on your PC, make a copy of the data and keep it in a different location.

Natural gemstone treatments

Just as wood furniture needs to be lacquered, so many gemstones require finishing before they are ready to be sold. As critical as good cutting and polishing, treatments have become an integral part of the modern gemstone industry. Akin to aging fine wine, most of the techniques used simply facilitate the beautiful end results of the Earth's natural processes.

While these treatments are taken as commonplace within the industry, the general public's awareness has been much lower. This page provides clear answers to common treatment questions.

Is the use of treatments globally accepted?

Yes, with close to 99% of the more popular gem types treated, all permanent techniques are universally accepted. As the majority of gemstones traded internationally have undergone some form of treatment, always assume treatment when purchasing gemstones. In fact, some techniques such as heating are centuries old - in all likelihood your grandmother's Ruby ring has been heat treated!

Are all the treatments used permanent?

Gems TV (with the exception of Emeralds that are treated with colourless oil or polymers) only supplies gemstone's whose treatments are permanent and stable.

Why are natural gemstones treated?

Most commonly used to improve the colour or appearance of the finished product, some gemstones simply would not exist in salable quantities without treatment. For example, heating greenish brown Zoisite to 600 degrees celsius produces the popular vibrant violet-blue Tanzanite. No heating, no Tanzanite! Please note that the term "natural gemstones" refers to those formed in the earth, whether or not they have been treated after mining - this is in distinct contrast to created or simulated gems.

Are All Gemstones Treated?

No, the following list includes gemstones that are NOT treated:

Alexandrite
Allanite
Amblygonite
Ametrine
Anatase
Andalusite
Apatite
Aventurine
Axinite
Azurite Malachite
Boracite
Brazilianite
Cassiterite
Chalcedony
Chrome Diopside
Chrysoberyl
Chrysocolla
Chrysoprase
Cinnabar
Clinohumite
Danburite
Diamond
Enstatite (Cats Eye)
Eosphorite
Epidote
Euclase
Fluorite
Gahnite
Garnet
Goshenite
Hematite
Herderite
Hiddenite
Howlite
Iolite
Jade
Kunzite
Kyanite
Labradorite
Larimar (Pectolite)
Manganotantalite
Mawsitsit
Moonstone
Natrolite
Nephrite
Obsidian
Oligoclase
Opal
Peridot
Pollucite
Prehnite
Pyrite
Quartz
Rhodonite
Rubellite
Rutile
Scapolite
Scolecite
Sellaite
Sillimanite (Cat's Eye)
Sinhalite
Sodalite
Sphalerite
Sphene
Spinel
Spodumene
Star Diopside
Star Sunstone
Staurolite
Sunstone
Tigers Eye
Topaz (White)
Tourmaline (Cats Eye)
Tsavorite
Unakite
Vesuvianite
Wilsonite

GEMSTONE TREATMENTS

Without heat treatment there would be no Tanzanite!

Does treatment affect a gem's value?

Interestingly, in some precious and semi-precious coloured gemstones there is no variation between the value of treated and untreated material. In fact, treating may even increase a gem's value. For example, when Zoisite is heated, vibrant violet Blue Tanzanite is created, commanding a far higher market price. However, high quality unheated Rubies and Sapphires are extremely rare and command a much higher market price. When purchasing high quality Rubies and Sapphires, please be aware that unheated material is almost non-existent. As a result, always purchase from a reliable supplier who guarantees their gemstones or have the seller's claim verified by a qualified expert.

What Gemstones Are Usually Treated & How?

The following table provides information on the treatments used for specific types, their purpose and frequency:

AMETHYST
Occasionally heated - Used to lighten colour and/or to remove smokiness.

AQUAMARINE
Occasionally heated - Used to remove yellow components to produce a purer blue colour with fewer yellow/green undertones.

CITRINE
Usually heated - This treatment produces/ increases colour.

EMERALD
Usually colourless oil or polymers - This treatment improves the appearance. If properly cared for, this treatment is permanent.

MORGANITE
Usually heated - This treatment eliminates yellow overtones.

PEARL
Occasionally applied - This treatment improves colour and colour uniformity.

PRASIOLITE
Often heated - This treatment improves colour.

QUARTZ
Occasionally heated - This treatment improves colour.

RUBY
Usually heated, occasionally with additives - Intensifies or lightens colour and/or improves colour uniformity and appearance.

SAPPHIRE
Usually heated, occasionally with additives - Intensifies or lightens colour and/or improves colour uniformity and appearance.

SAPPHIRE (GREEN)
Usually heated - This treatment improves the colour.

TANZANITE
Almost always heated - This treatment produces the violet-blue colours for which the gem is known.

TOPAZ (EXCEPT WHITE)
Usually heated, diffused or coated - Used to improve colour intensity or to produce unique colours.

ZIRCON (BLUE & WHITE)
Always heated - Used to improve colour.

Gemological Institute of America (GIA)
World Headquarters
The Robert Mouawad Campus
5345 Armada Drive
Carlsbad,
California 92008
USA
Tel: 760-603-4000

Gübelin Gem Lab Ltd.
For International customers, arguably one of the world's best valuation companies and the most respected one in Switzerland is:
Gübelin Gem Lab Ltd.
Maihofstrasse 102
6006 Lucerne
Switzerland
Or Contact us at:
Tel: (+ 41) 41 / 429 17 17
Fax: (+ 41) 41 / 429 17 34
www.gubelinlab.com

International Coloured Gemstone Association
19 West 21st Street,
Suite 705
New York,
N.Y. 10010-6805
USA
Tel: 212-620-0900

SafeGuard Quality Assurance Ltd
PO Box 8706
Newhall Street
Birmingham
B3 1FH
Tel: 0121 236 2122
Fax: 0121 236 2128

USEFUL CONTACTS

These independent valuers have been recommended to us by our happy customers and are not endorsed by Gems TV. Gems TV have contacted the individual jewellers and they have given us permission to include their details. If you know of a valuer that offers an efficient, swift and cost effective valuation, that you would like to recommend, please email their details to valuations@GemsTV.com

---

Stanleys The Jewellers (Ring resizing)
113 Vyse Street, Birmingham B18 6LP
Tel: 0121 236 7806

A.J.R Jewellers
Dinnington, Sheffield S25 2PN
Tel: 01909 568452

Watling Goldsmiths of Lacock
15 East Street, Lacock SN15 2LF
Tel: 01249 730422

Crystal Needs Valuations
P.O. Box 181, Ormskirk L39 0WZ
Tel: 07837 064 277

Gem World Jewellers
16 Seamoor Road, Bournmouth,
Dorset BH4 9AR
Tel: 01202 761764

Offords Jewellers
Hampshire SO239AP
Tel: 01962 867772

Andrew Jones
38-39 Stodman Street, Newark
Nottingham NG24 1AW
Tel: 01636679638

Brooker & Breeze Goldsmith Ltd
27 High Street, Oxfordshire OX10 0BU
Tel: 01491 835050

INDEX

INDEX

ACKNOWLEDGEMENTS

Gems TV would like to thank the following team members for their contribution to this guide:

(in alphabetical order)
Alex Sharp, Ceri James-Gerrard, Clive Bryant, Debby Cavill, Don Kogen, Dylan Bartlett, Gavin Linsell, John Bennett, Jo Wheeler, Lee Roberts, Mary Baladad, Michelle Duggins, Paul Bridges, Steve Ashton, Steve Bennett and Vicky Hall.

Plus, thanks to all the Gems TV presenters and our skilled craftsmen at our Design Centre in Thailand.

Many thanks also go to our customers who have allowed for their valuations to be printed.

How to obtain Gems TV jewellery:

In the UK watch us 24 hours a day on:
Sky Guide 646 and NTL 177

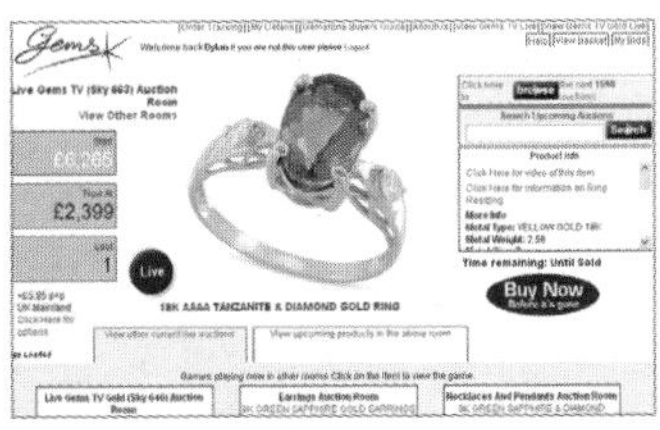

In Europe visit our website: www.GemsTV.com

In America and Asia visit our website:
www.Thaigem.com